SOMEONE

BIBLIOGRAPHY
Robert Pinget

Entre Fantoine et Agapa La Tour du
Feu, 1951; Les Éditions de
Minuit* Paris, 1966
Mahu ou le Matériau Paris, 1952
Le Renard et la Boussole Éd.
Gallimard, Paris, 1955
Graal Flibuste Paris, 1956
Baga Paris, 1958
Le Fiston Paris, 1959

*Lettre Morte*** Paris, 1959
*La Manivelle*** Paris, 1960
Clope au dossier Paris, 1961
*Ici ou Ailleurs*** Paris, 1961
*L'Hypothèse*** Paris, 1961
*Architruc*** Paris, 1961
L'Inquisitoire Paris, 1962

Autour de Mortin Paris, 1965
Quelqu'un Paris, 1965
Le Libéra Paris, 1968

Passacaille Paris, 1969

*Identité suivi de Abel et Bela*** Paris,
1971
Fable Paris 1971
*Paralchimie*** Paris 1973
Cette Voix Paris, 1975
L'Apocryphe Paris, 1980
Monsieur Songe Paris, 1982
Le Harnais Paris, 1984

Between Fantoine and Agapa
Red Dust, 1982

Mahu or the Material Calder, 1966

Baga Calder, 1967
No Answer Calder, 1961; *Mr. Levert*
Grove Press, 1961
Dead Letter Calder, 1963
The Old Tune Calder, 1963

Clope Calder, 1963
The Hypothesis Calder, 1967
Architruc Calder, 1967
The Inquisitory Calder and Grove
Press, 1966
About Mortin Calder, 1967
Someone Red Dust, 1984
The Libera Me Domine Calder,
1972; Red Dust, 1978
Recurrent Melody Calder, 1975
Passacaglia Red Dust, 1978

Fable Calder; Red Dust, 1980

That Voice Red Dust, 1982

*Les Éditions de Minuit is the French publisher of all the works unless otherwise noted.
**play

SOMEONE

Robert Pinget

**Translated by
Barbara Wright**

 Red Dust   New York   1984

Published by Red Dust, Inc. All rights reserved.

Library of Congress Card Number   83-063101
ISBN   0-87376-04303
The publication of this book has been supported in part by a grant from the
National Endowment for the Arts in Washington D.C., a Federal Agency.

SOMEONE

I t was here, that bit of paper, on the table, by the jar, it can't have flown. Has she been tidying up? Has she put it with the others? I've looked everywhere, I've gone through everything, I've wasted my entire morning, I just can't find it. It's infuriating, infuriating. I've been telling her for years not to touch this table. It lasts for a couple of days and then the third day she starts all over again and I can't find anything. It seems it's the same everywhere, in every house, in every household. Then we ought to do away with maids, or women. Personally I could easily do without them. I have my little things, I have what I call my little work, I can do without everyone, I can live on my own. The grub part isn't complicated and the rest doesn't exist. Work is the only thing that matters. How true, letting yourself be messed about all your life by people who tidy up your papers. I ought to have organized my life differently but there you are, you've got embroiled in existence, you don't even know how. I haven't any intention of talking about my existence but I'll probably have to. It's so totally uninteresting, so totally dull. Makes you wonder if it's true. Makes you believe that you don't choose. Personally I've known for a long time that you don't choose but there are people who maintain that you do, that you're responsible, that you're free, a load of crap. And they develop arguments to use against you, they prove things to you by A plus B, they drive you into a corner. I'm there all the time. They corner me every time. So when it comes to developing my own arguments, that doesn't take a

1

moment, I haven't any. I try to get started on a chain of reasoning, to finesse, to make them believe I know all this and that, that I've had experience. I talk about misfortune, bad luck, things that get in your way, that cut the grass from under your feet. I try to give some sort of form to what I say, my references are all spurious, I mix up the thinkers, the mystics, and people immediately realize that I'm drivelling, that I haven't any culture, nothing, merely pretensions. But that's just where they're wrong, I haven't any pretensions, they force me into having them. It isn't only once, it's a thousand times that they've shoved me into this situation. We oughtn't to let ourselves get caught up, we ought to tell them all to go to hell and then retire to the country but we're always telling ourselves that it isn't the right moment, that we need other people, that we do have to live in society, a whole lot of affectations that can trap us for good. And that do trap us. You still know that you don't need anything, that you have your little work, that you can make your own chow, you tell yourself so all the time, you despise the lot of them but you stay with them.

All this for that bit of paper. I can't carry on without that bit of paper. Or can it have blown away? Did I leave my window open? That's possible with this heat but I surely didn't leave the paper without putting something on it. The ashtray, the magnifying glass, something. I'm so careful. I'm always telling myself that my papers might blow away. I can't have left it like that. Unless someone disturbed me? And asked me to go downstairs pronto?

I can already feel that I'm going to have to talk about my existence. This bores me horribly. I avoid it as far as possible. I've even written it down in detail so as to get rid of it, so as not to have to come back to it. I thought that might be a kind of exorcism or conjuration. Like when you touch wood, for instance. But it isn't true. There's always a detail that's escaped you and you fall into the trap at the first opportunity. Someone's talking to you about something and you suddenly say, that's like me, that happened to me yesterday, and you explain, you clarify, you reassure yourself, you're just coming to the next subject, don't get impatient, everything has to be in order first. Impossible. You're back in your own caca, impossible to get out of it. As if you forever had to have it within reach so as to smear it all over. That isn't what I meant to say. As if your existence had forever to be made up of a nice compact package that you could pick up there and then and carry around wherever you went. And it isn't even a simile, I oughtn't to say as if, there's no if about it. It's the way things happen. Your existence in a travelling bag, neatly packed, neatly catalogued, so's you have everything you need just in case. And you never stop packing your bag, you're forever packaging something. Even when you're saying it's a lovely day. There's something in my bag that isn't in its place. You re-unpack, you re-arrange, you re-package, you're all set once again but then what do you know, it isn't a lovely day any more, you get wet, you're soaked to the skin. So you re-open your bag. It's almost as if you do it on purpose. As if you're waiting every second to re-open it.

I say that but I really don't know, maybe it's all spurious, like my mystics. And then I talk and talk, please excuse me, I'm not used to it. It's true that I'm always busy with my little work, I don't speak to anyone any more, not seriously, I mean. My little index cards, my little notes, my bits of paper. In the end they swallow me whole, they make me lose all sense of reality. Reality. Basically I'm not interested in it. I've had my fill. In the old days, when I wasn't doing my little work, I was like everyone else, I talked, I had experiences, I lived, as they say. I gave myself a pain in the ass. That's the precise expression. Or rather, not quite. I gave myself a pain in the ass but I was all the time telling myself that I was going about things the wrong way, that I was biased, that I didn't see things as they are, that I could get a whole lot more out of them and that things would change. Things and people, I mean. Especially people. So I made the pleasure last, if that's what you call it. I wallowed in other people's caca, telling myself that I wasn't seeing clearly, that I needed to pay more attention, and also to be nicer, to forget myself a little, to like them a little, to help them a little, to get them to open up a little. Shit. The more they opened up the more of it there was. There was a moment when I couldn't stand it any longer, I was suffocating. So I retreated into my own.

There's no point in talking about the travelling bag again, I shan't be able to get away from it. Even if it's a spurious idea and things happen differently, I've decided that it suits me. I haven't finished repacking it.

I'm even going to start right away, with that bit of paper. With as few details as possible at first, they'll come soon enough.

I got up at eight as usual, I put on my dressing gown and went down to drink my tea, I went upstairs again, and that was that. I got dressed, and sat down at my table.

I opened my manuscript, well, what I call my manuscript, I read what I'd done yesterday, I crossed it all out and started again from the beginning. At one moment I had to check something and I opened my little card index. The information wasn't there. I looked among the other papers, they're all over the table, I sorted them all, read them all through, meticulously, even though I knew already that I was doing too much and that the paper I was looking for wasn't there, just to be quite sure. Nothing. So I went downstairs again, I asked her when she had moved my things. She told me that she'd never moved them since I'd told her. That was a couple of days ago, right. But before, before. She swore she'd tidied up, that was all. But what does that mean, tidied up? It means gathering up all the bits of paper lying around and putting them in a pile next to the card index. I didn't like the expression lying around, nothing lies around on my table, everything is in its place, in its precise place, the moment anyone touches it I can't find a thing. As witness. She re-swore, I re-asked, and before the last time, and before that, in the end she just didn't know any more, she was losing her temper. I went upstairs again, looked everywhere again, under the bed, under the furniture, between all the pages in the manuscript, well, what I call the manuscript, there was nothing. At that moment I really must have told myself that something had happened. A draught for example. Knowing that it was impossible but that I had to do something, I couldn't stay there and do nothing, I surely didn't stay and fret at my table the whole morning. No. I surely did something. I must have gone down into the garden to see. Let's see. I can't find that paper, I get upset, I think about the draught, I look out of the window. That's it. It's coming back to me. I went down into the garden.

The main thing is for it all to be orderly in my mind. I don't want to embark on this story, I'm calling it a story, now, on this exposé, without taking my precautions. This has happened to me before. In the end you find yourself in quite the wrong place. Or rather, you don't find yourself anywhere at all. You're exposed to the elements, quite defenseless, no sweater, no armour, it's armour you need and you catch your death. At all events you're terribly messed up. I don't want any more of that. I want to keep all my wits about me and say what I feel like saying. Had I already begun my little work at that moment, at those moments? Probably not. Difficult to remember. Yes of course though, I had. Then I must have gone on telling the story of my life in order to get rid of it even though I knew it didn't work? What a cross it is to have no memory. Complications already. When I'd got started so nicely, almost gaily. But we mustn't let things get us down. We must keep all our wits about as, as I said before. Hold on, hang on.

I went down into the garden, then, I went the rounds of it. The steps, the flower bed, the slope down to the cellar, nothing. Then the shed, I even went into that, you never know, I searched it thoroughly, nothing. It could have blown in there, the door's almost always open, I have to put up a fight to get them to shut it at least at night, it makes things look untidy. Next the shrubbery along the wall up to the gate, it doesn't take long to go the rounds. The paper wasn't there. I thought it might have got stuck in the chestnut tree, I examined it thoroughly from below, it isn't all that tall, it's been truncated on account of the electricity cables that pass overhead. But I was already sure the paper wasn't there. I'm always doing things like that, though I know there's no point. I wonder what this is due to. You check three times that a door or a window is closed, or the gas or electricity switched off, you know perfectly well that it is and yet you do it again more than three times, even, telling yourself that the time before you maybe didn't see properly or you were thinking of something else. In short, the surer you are, the more you check. This very quickly goes from bad to worse and you could spend your whole time checking the gas. This must happen to people who don't have much to do, the organism has to use up its energy and it uses it up like that, through the nerves. It certainly must be the nerves.

I notice that I've already more or less described the frame my life fits into with this room and that garden. Must I got into further detail? What a bore, what a bore. It's not at all lack of goodwill, it's not laziness. It's fear, it's distress. Because I've already done it several times, as I've just said. Once the frame has been put up it has to be filled in and it's your existence you put into it, what else could you put into it. And then it starts all over again exactly like the previous time, you want to give an overall picture, you want to go too fast and the net result... Let's try not to think about it too much, even though we know the result will be the same. Let's at least try to go slowly.

It's going to be difficult, I shan't know what to say. These temptations, these pitfalls. If only I could get rid of that idea, of that fear, and simply talk about the bit of paper I'm looking for, without being afraid of anything. But I certainly can't count on that, I know myself. The entire frame is going to come into it, and life as well. I give simplicity up as lost. Not that I'm complicated, for heaven's sake. Nothing but little worries, little prospects, little satisfactions. My work above all, my manuscript, well, what I call my manuscript. It's a dissertation on plants. Not at all technical, not at all literary. Observations I've made. I still haven't spoken of a quarter, of a tenth of our local plants, there are so many of them and you have to give so many details. Details I really care about, my very own. No method, just details. Method, that's another thing I've had my fill of. It falsifies everything, it upsets everything. I had a go at making use of it to tell my life story and you know where that got me. I had a go at it in the beginning for my plants, but instead of stimulating me it sent me to sleep. When you have to consult plant guides and botany books, thanks a lot. All the fragrance of nature disappears. No no, that's all over. I do my little work the way I like, putting in personal remarks. That's what's needed. Personal remarks, not to be afraid of giving your own opinion. It's also a danger, because you run the risk of talking about yourself, but the moment you feel you're on the slippery slope, quick, you go back to the flower or the leaf.

I adore nature. It's crazy how you can forget it when you're working in an office. I'd never have thought you could miss it so much. You get accustomed to a timetable, to your work, to your organization, as they call it. You organize your life as a function, as they call it, of your work and of your leisure, when you have any. Leisure. How frightful. I'm talking about the leisure I had before, before, when I was working in an office. And those conversations in cafés, what a waste of time. All that because you're trying to be sociable, to live in society, to take an interest in other people, to be open to people. We know where that gets us. And what have we done with nature? We don't even know that she's still there. With her flowers, her leaves, her insects And the day when we do realize, it's often too late. Fortunately, fortunately I escaped from that hell. I managed it just in time. When I saw that I was losing sight of nature, just like that, when I happened to be going for a walk, and God knows how rarely I used to go for walks, I immediately called a halt. I turned my back on office work and came here. I must in all honesty say that I didn't take the decision entirely of my own accord. Things helped me. I was so terribly pissed off by the things you know about that my cup was full. So, in short, I overflowed here.

Here. I've got myself back to the frame again. Do I really have to go on describing it? Easy does it!

It isn't the proper country, alas, nor is it solitude. I'm still embroiled with other people. But even so it's not like an office, I must be fair. It's a guest house. In the suburbs. The real countryside begins a few kilometers away. I've been here, oh, I don't know any more, about ten years. It's always ten years ago that people have done something. It was at the moment when I couldn't bear it any longer, when my cup was about to overflow. A friend of mine was in the same situation and he inveigled me into his project. I had a bit of a nest egg, so had he, we put them together and bought this guest house. Well, this house. It was Gaston's idea to take in paying guests. I had to agree, we had to eat. A few guests, the minimum. And that was that.

The garden is ghastly. Twenty meters by twenty. In the middle, the chestnut tree, and at the far end the shed, which is just a cubby hole made of planks. You can't sit in the garden on account of the factory next door. Black dust all over and the small of burned fat coming from the canteen. It's a pity, in summer. All year long as it is we're cooped up together in the craproom, we'd enjoy being spread out a bit somewhere else. At first we tried cleaning up the garden every day but what a job. A greasy dust. Even just cleaning the chairs and the table took so long. We gave up.

I genuinely wonder, and I shall wonder to the end, whether I'm doing the right thing in going straight to the heart of the matter. I can already sense the danger lying in wait for me. After the frame, its inhabitants. And with the inhabitants, me. I shall never be able to talk calmly about their affairs, nor even to describe them, without scrutinizing myself. Everything's linked, everything's entangled, everything's contradictory. Just the very fact of having talked about Gaston irritates me. I'd intended not to mention any names. Merely the proprietor, room number one, room number two. It would have remained anonymous, a bit vague, a bit elusive. The culture medium, without going into detail. But something tells me that that might have been boring. Can you afford to be boring? I rather think not. When people are interrogating us we have to do our utmost to answer as best we can. What am I saying, interrogating. Who's interrogating me? No one, for God's sake! Don't let anyone come and tell me that I answer questions. Because that has been said. That has been said in the past. Apropos of my other lives, when I was trying to get rid of them. He answers questions, as you see. That must be the police. It sounds like the police, he's obliged to answer, he's forced, he's cornered. That sort of nonsense. I certainly must have gone the wrong way about it in that composition. To have been so very wide of the mark, to give such a wrong impression. It's exasperating. Never enough talent. In short, I don't want to give the impression that I answer questions. Not give the impression, even though I do answer, I've just unwittingly said that I was being interrogated. That escaped me. What a bore. One more thing to explain, but just as well, actually, it delays the entry into the heart of the matter.

This impression, and it is only an impression, must come from a long way away. Even at the very beginning, at the time of my first composition, I had the feeling that I was answering. There was a vague question somewhere and I was answering it. More than vague, and not even an answer, you understand. Not a sentence like where are you going or what are you doing. Unformulated but present. Or maybe so badly formulated that I took it for a question? That's possible. I'd have done better to listen more carefully, to make a couple of attempts at it. That would have saved me from answering, if it wasn't necessary. And besides, maybe at this very moment I'm fantasizing, trying to cover myself, as I've suffered so much from those unsuccessful compositions. Somewhere I'm trying to blame it on that interrogation. It's possible. At all events I still had an extremely vague impression that I was answering. An infinitely vague feeling. Feeling. Fog. I can't find the word. And what's more, still because of my defective ear, there I was, hearing, or thinking I was hearing, answers. A real Joan of Arc. It's painful to realize all this after the event. To have embarked on this dialogue of the deaf and not to be able to extricate yourself. More than painful. Whereas one could have gone in for such interesting things, mountaineering, running, I don't know. To find yourself on the wrong track like that, in the middle of life, stupidly, and to spend your time wondering where you could have gone wrong. Because now, however much I quibble and finesse, I really do feel I've gone wrong. There's nothing to be done now. Not even the impossible.

Mustn't lose my head. Everything must be in order, under control. I began this exposé with a question I myself had asked. Which isn't the same thing. Where is that paper. I must keep coming back to it. I mustn't lose sight of it.

While I was searching the garden something must have happened. I have a sort of recollection of a hiatus, a diversion. Did I stick my nose through the gate and start daydreaming, looking out into the street? Did I imagine what was going on in the garden opposite? You can't see, there's a wall there too. Above it on the right there are some apricot trees and a scarecrow. There's a weathercock on the roof of the house, in the form of a locomotive. The neighbour is a retired railroad worker. We never see him. Or rather, *I* never see him. We probably go out at different times. Because I go herborizing. But some of the guests have seen him and even spoken to him. Unless I've got it wrong and it was someone else. Fraternizing and gossiping with neighbours bores me more than it should. Thought it might provide me with some unimportant bits of information which might perhaps amuse me. But as caca is never very far away, I fight shy of it in advance. And I say that the neighbours bore me. Then why imagine what they get up to behind their walls? Incomprehensible. I have an incomprehensible nature. Because I can only imagine squalid stories when I think about them, and yet I still imagine them. Maybe I get them out of my mind more easily afterwards? Probably. But it's still incomprehensible because they have strictly nothing to offer me.

Unless I spoke to someone from the guest house? That must be it. Someone who was going out. Who? I don't know, I don't know. It's already irritating me. Yet I really do have to answer myself. The maid. It must have been the maid. She was going out and she must have said something to me. Going out where? Shopping, she was going shopping as she does every morning. Ah yes, it's coming back to me. Marie was going shopping, she saw me searching the garden, she asked me what I was looking for now. I told her that bit of paper, that goddam paper you tidied up. She didn't like that. My tone was unpleasant. Instead of shutting her up, an unpleasant tone nettles her, she gets in a huff, she answers back and there's no end to it. I've known this for ages, but I forget every time. Instead of controlling myself I let myself go, and heave-ho, there's a scene. Personally it's so foreign to my nature to answer back that I forget. An unpleasant tone of voice paralyzes me right away and I make myself scarce. With her, it's the opposite. I could always have avoided getting into a shouting match with her. But at the moment I forget, Marie's temperament goes out of my mind and I have to put up with a good ten minutes of it. Though I detest, but detest, such things. Yes, I remember perfectly, when she'd run out of backchat she finally threw in my face the word trifle, that I was only interested in trifles, something along those lines. It's charming when you hear your whole future demolished at one stroke. It took my breath away. It choked me. My back to the wall. She went off to do her shopping and I was left without a leg to stand on. She was right, the bitch, my little work was trifling. Spending your whole time examining minutiae under a microscope, was that an occupation? It was shameful, disgusting. While other people are struggling, while they, poor wretches, are fighting for survival, I was playing at being an amateur botanist. Completely demolished, that's what I was. But this wasn't the first time, fortunately. I knew the trick that enables us to resurface. Not really a trick, in the end it became instinctive. At the time you feel completely washed out, you think you're even lousier than ever, but gradually the light dawns, your strength returns. You re-reason with yourself. Instinctively you re-reason with yourself. You re-tell yourself that you've had your time of fighting for survival , of struggling, and that you've earned a bit of peace and quiet. You re-persuade yourself. Instinctively you re-persuade yourself and you get back on your feet again. It has long since stopped being reasoning, it's the instinct of self-preservation. But all the same it's stupid to let yourself be demolished every time by a Marie, and to have to resurface every time. This sort of activity wears you out. It undermines you. I realize this because it makes me hungry. I simply have to eat something. Well, it must be that. After the knockout blow I went and ate something. I went back into the house and into the kitchen. It can only be that.

This already adds up to a lot of activity and a lot of people. Careful. And I came out with the name Marie on purpose, it didn't just escape me. That much less for the culture medium, careful. Maybe it would be better to start again from the moment when I was searching the garden, and ask myself whether something else might have happened. I've talked about the neighbour, the weathercock, and Marie, but maybe it was a bit vague. I say that I recollect, that it's coming back to me, but you should beware. I'm overdoing it a bit, I'm dissembling. I have a head like a sieve, that's my weakness, and I know it. But recollecting tires me so much that sometimes I say, that's it, it's coming back to me, but it isn't. Not that I want to deceive anyone, oh no. I have a horror of lying. But fatigue too produces a kind of instinct of self-preservation, and then just try and see clearly. You no longer know whether you've had a fit of abstraction for a second or whether you really do remember. The way you have to fight against your own nature, it's unbelievable. Maybe I let myself go just now and my instinct was speaking for me. In this instance I don't want to let it get the upper hand. I want to keep all my wits about me and say what I have to say. Let's forget about the pitfall of truth for the moment. Let's stick to duty. What I am duty bound to say. At least we always know where our duty lies. It's whatever is the biggest pain in the ass. Very simple.

Right. To resume. I get to the steps. I look to left and to right. I walk down the steps, I go over towards the cellar, looking in the flower bed. As there's nothing in it it doesn't take long. At the very beginning we tried to put things in it, we planted touch-me-not balsams, larkspurs, sweet williams, flowers nobody had ever seen and which tempted us on the seed packets. They came up all right, you couldn't say they didn't germinate or even flower, but they were such a sorry sight, so pathetic. They all turned into tiny little flowers, I wouldn't exactly call them wizened but unattractive, too stumpy, too sparse. Nothing like their photo on the packet. It had taken us for a ride, that packet. Moreover, the dust didn't spare them. We watered them well, that washed them, we felt sorry for them, but we can't have kept it up, given the result. Yes, touch-me-not balsams, I remember. Just the very name made you covet them. Well, they were a disaster. Unless, maybe, you plant a whole lot of them, all squeezed up, with lots of manure, and they grow, and they ramify, I don't know. So nothing in the flower bed. I get to the slope leading down to the cellar door, I look, I turn right towards the shed, I go into the shed. At this point, to be honest, I shall have to itemize everything in the shed, which I inspected and walked around. But I don't want to go in for any more inventories. I used to in the past, so conscientiously, so patiently! In my other exposés, to help myself concentrate, hoping that it would clear the way for my unconscious, that it would open up some paths towards the essential. Nix. Totally useless. Objects are no good at all when you're aiming at the soul. At first glance we might imagine they could help us to make up our minds, to concentrate, as I said before. Crap. You get caught up in the game, you polish the description, you get a kick out of it, but the net result is that you're back to square one. You haven't advanced in knowledge by a single step. You don't know any better than before either why you do what you do or where you're going. Now I consider that that's the essential. Mind you, when you describe other things, as for instance your moods, the state of your soul, as they say, when you analyze your desires, you don't do any better. Nor your actions, either, I know that too, I've had that experience too. But it's more, how can I put it, more noble, more difficult. I was going to say more human. In short, no inventories. Every so often I'll describe an object, yes, all right, but only for the pleasure of it. Let's say for relaxation, to make a break. And then, now I come to think of it, if I were to describe all the objects that surround me the frame would be all set and raring to go and the only thing left for me to do would be to plonk my behind down in the middle and make my confession. That would be pointless, I don't want any of that.

After the shed I carried on along the wall, looking into the shrubbery. Also ghastly. Aucubas black with dust. I believe we used to water them too in the beginning. Yes, it's coming back to me. It really is, this time, you don't need to beware. We used to spray them with the sprinkler we bought for the purpose. It's in the shed now, the sprinkler, well, the hose. At the back on the left.

I get to the gate. Here I really do have to concentrate. No approximations. I'm following the same procedure as before because I believe there was a hiatus, a diversion. I *must* find out. Did I inspect the chestnut tree before or after? I must have done that after. What can have happened then, let's think, unless I was daydreaming about the garden opposite. Did I look up at our house to see whether anyone was observing me? I hate being observed. I'm getting to hate it more and more. I loathe it. This must be because I realize that my obsessions are becoming more pronounced, and I still have a sense of the ridiculous. And that's one sense that would have done better to desert me, like a lot of others. The only ones I'm left with are the useless ones, the harmful ones. How can I find the way, with all this, to behave intelligently, or at least with elegance. I'm going to sink back into my obsessions and my verifications, all the while hating people to realize it and continuing to live under observation. I'm quite sure they observe me. I have some examples which I shall cite. When I say under observation, I mean it in the clinical sense. They know I'm on the downward path and they discuss it amongst themselves. It's intolerable. But the most intolerable thing is not to be able to react. The sense of the ridiculous, amour-propre, that's what makes people suffer. More and more I tell myself that without amour-propre we wouldn't suffer. I'm quite willing for people still to have grand passions which have nothing to do with amour-propre, but there can't be very many of them left, you must be able to count them on your fingers. Grand passions! How I would have liked to have known that. It must be passionately exciting. Nothing counts any moe except the loved object or the goal to be achieved.

I was being observed. I don't dare say that it's coming back to me. I

must have been under observation. Marie was observing me from one
of the bedrooms she was cleaning. I saw her moving back from the
window when I looked up. Or did she stay there just to taunt me? She
did stay there, quite so, the bitch. She knows I hate it, she stayed there
on purpose. Caught unawares, I came out with an idiotic phrase we
used to say at school, I asked her, have I grown horns? What did she
answer, let me remember exactly. She didn't answer. She shrugged her
shoulders, which was even more contemptuous. And she stayed there,
leaning on the windowsill. I can still see her. What a nerve. What a filthy
nerve. It shut me up. Did it shut me up? Of course it did, I didn't say any
more and I pretended to be examining the chestnut tree, as if I was
looking for the nest. That was at least plausible. We'd been talking about
a nest in the chestnut tree. So I was trying to see this nest. What had we
said it was? We didn't know. Chaffinches or blackbirds. So I searched
and searched, I walked around the tree. It wasn't for my paper, it was the
nest. Obviously I didn't see it. I darted a quick glance to find out whether
Marie was still at the window but she'd gone. She couldn't care less, she
was going on with her housework, she'd humiliated me and that
satisfied her. Bitch. Do away with maids and women. Do our little
work, our little research, and let them leave us in peace.

What did I do next. Did my amour-propre allow me to go on
searching for my paper? Marie might reappear at any moment and
humiliate me at any moment. I had to give up and sit down under the
chestnut tree. This was in itself pretty unusual, my trousers would be all
black, but I needed to think, to ask myself what I was going to do. I may
perhaps have wiped the chair with a leaf. Did I stay there like that for
long? Because more and more, these days, I find myself stuck on a chair,
and time goes by. That's what they call absences. Wrongly. They're
presences, these whatsits, heavy presences, tons of presence. And don't
let anyone tell me that we don't know what we're thinking about in
these moments. We're thinking about one thing, always the same.
Afterwards we can repeat everything we thought about it. Without
being very wrong because it's always the same thing. Personally, at that
moment it was my paper, it could only have been my paper. How it
must have disappeared and what I was going to do. That was when
Marie really must have gone out to do her shopping. But I have to be
sure. I don't want to keep repeating myself, even thought it's extremely
agreeable. I want to get ahead.

Marie went out shopping. But why, actually? Was it her shopping time? What it is not to want to tire yourself and to say it's coming back to me. Afterwards you're driven mad, you have to start all over again. If it was housework time it wasn't shopping time. Unless I stayed under my chestnut tree for an hour? Or unless Marie had been doing the last bedroom and had gone out immediately after? All my wits. No flights of fancy. Let's start again.

I got up at eight, and went down to drink my tea in the refectory. We call the dining room the refectory, this irritates some people, it sounds like a monastery or a boarding school but so what, we've got into the habit. Someone came out with the word at the beginning, maybe Gaston as a joke, and it stuck. I went upstairs again straightaway, I got dressed and sat down at my table. Quarter to nine at the very outside. I read over what I'd produced the day before, and started writing. I missed my paper right away, I looked for it on the table and around the room. Quarter past nine at the very outside. I'm not going to start perorating about the time which we waste, which we lose sight of, which just disappears, which we imagine, or which we tout for more or less dishonestly, it irritates me. And anyway it's as plain as the nose on your face and doesn't interest anyone any more. No, I simply want to know what time I went down into the garden. By the time I'd made the decision it must have been nine twenty. Going the rounds of the garden and the shed didn't take me more than five minutes. Let's call it half past nine at the outside when the bitch stationed herself at the window. Well yes, then, she would have been finishing the last bedroom. She must have come down immediately afterwards, it was time for her to go shopping. That suits me. It was Marie all right. Otherwise I should have had to come out with some more names, and to remember which ones later on... They'll emerge quite soon enough.

Did Marie merely look at me on my chair or did she say something to me? Did she perhaps say what are you looking for? Apparently not, more likely what are you doing there. Why does the word trifle stick in my mind? If she asked me what are you doing, I certainly replied, nothing, to cut it short. She probably asked me what were you looking for just now and I replied that bit of paper you tidied up, in the tone of voice we know about. Maybe that. But what if I had only imagined that she was going to ask me and only imagined that she would then reply, your trifle? Because she'd said it before, several times even, and each time it got me into the same state. This is already becoming tedious. I'll have to simplify. Not tell myself too often what I might have imagined.

Have confidence in what comes back to you not always in the first place let's say but at any rate in the second, and which as such is positive. I'll go no further than the trifle formulated, that's safer. It's already almost a choice, it's bordering on the dishonest. You'll have to excuse me. I need to badger myself a bit, to shake myself up. Then my exposé will gain in clarity. Which is easily conceivable. And for me, to conceive would rather be to stop myself. Anyone might think I was talking about a brilliant brain in a state of effervescence. No, stop myself doing you know what.

Putting the finishing touches to things, that's what I like best. I might even say that I adore it. Precision—what a marvel! But people don't understand. They think it's beauty or magnificence or love or God knows what. It's precision. For my part, it enthralls me. Finding the right word, finding the exact word—it's divine. I must say in passing that it's often the word caca that is the most precise. We need to have a bit of a laugh.

And now I'm already regretting my kind of choice. To give the impression of arbitrariness right from the start. If that brings increased clarity, well, fine, but what about precision? To decide, because after all I did decide, that it was at that moment that Marie said trifle to me, in the first place it *is* dishonest, it isn't merely bordering on it, and then and above all it's imprecise. I can't leave it at that. I'll have to start again. And besides, this principle of clarity is ludicrous. Anything that is properly conceived doesn't get stated, it gets done. It's because we don't understand anything about it that we talk. If we understood, we'd be only too pleased to keep quiet. The very fact of stating something, whether clearly or not, means that we are in the... the you-know-what. It's when we're opening up that we see clearly. And when it's finished we wipe ourselves and we shut our traps. That's bordering on vulgarity. I have no desire to be vulgar, I shall avoid it as far as possible. But what has to be has to be.

I only hope I don't get disgusted too quickly with what I'm doing here. This exposé. I'm scared stiff. I'm praying to God. I don't want to talk about my life in it, as I've already said, but I have a strong suspicion that it's going to be like my previous compositions. I'm getting rid of something. If I get rid of it too quickly, I mean if I get disgusted with it right away, I shall have to start the whole thing again. Starting again is martyrdom. To make something last without getting disgusted is also a martyrdom but it's quite different. It's nothing, in comparison. It can even be a kind of pleasure. It makes a change from my botany. In short, I have to get rid of it but at the same time make it last, at the same time get pleasure out of it. I must seem obscure to people who aren't used to finishing touches. But when you come down to it, without wishing to offend anybody, it isn't them I'm aiming at. The people who will be prepared to follow me will be the ones who like finishing touches. They must already have realized the kind that are in store for them. I take a great many precautions for very little, that's a bad sign. I can already foresee that it's going to be deadly dull, and this bothers me, I don't like boring people. If only I could talk about something else! My God, I'd throw myself into it body and soul! Just out of kindness, out of philanthropy. But there it is, I can't. In another sense, maybe it's a good sign? Wouldn't it prove that I don't do things lightly, that I want to be authentic, my real self, so that people can detect my real sui generis odour? Pah. The moment you start trying to be profound, conscientious... How does one achieve good work? Not think too much about it, probably. Think you're not thinking about it. Fortunately, fortunately, I'm not the only inhabitant of the guest house. If I feel disgust creeping up on me I can always go on to other subjects, to other natives. So here I am, counting on them, now. When I didn't even want to mention them. It's disconcerting. And this anxiety to be oneself, how pretentious! I do even so have pretensions. Can there be such a thing as an honest pretension? I want to believe that there can. But anyway, if there can't, so what. Let's forget about pretensions and concentrate on honesty. Forget, once again. Dishonesty, once again. The dishonesty of wanting to be honest. What a shittery.

In one of my other lives, hang on, I've only ever had one, I mean my other exposés, I said I was king of my own filth. Which came to the same thing, reading between the lines. In short, I observe that I'm not out of it. Can one be responsible for an observation? Of course, alas. At least, in the current acceptance. *I* say that one is not responsible for anything. But whatever you do, don't ask me to prove it. I don't want to spend my life with my back to the wall. Because the people who are, with their backs to the wall, they're there to be shot. Get away, with your foul rifles. Get away. There are meadows to gambol in, and I have just as much right to them as anyone else. I want my place in the sun. For the moment it's in this garden. Very funny.

And then, on reflection, I'm not sorry that the others are there. I'm willing to talk about them. I don't want to seem to be avoiding them, only to say, every time I come across a name, ah, here's another name. All in all it's thanks to them that I can live a life of ease. They pay. I'm not denying that Gaston and I went to a lot of trouble to organize it all, it was even epic. We put a lot of our energies into it, and money too. All I had, all he had. Which didn't stop the others falling for it, since they came. And once again, they pay. It's thanks to them that we eat. We don't give credit in the joint, or if we do it's only exceptionally and for a short time. I have a duty towards them so I shall talk about them. But without any great haste. All my wits about me. Do I mean with my head, not my heart? I wouldn't mind. When I let myself go I get really mawkish. Which would imply that I love them? My goodness, I don't know. Now and then. When I feel my glottis vibrating or my eyelids oozing I think I love them. And a minute later I feel like vomiting or lashing out. Is that love? At any rate I know it gives me a pain in the ass to talk about them. It can't be love. Lovers ramble on freely about love and what they love. Honestly, I don't believe I have ever loved. Or if it did happen to me I didn't talk about it. Unless you lump it together with the kind of frantic agony of not being able to fuck? When someone has thrown you over, for instance. That, yes, I've known that. But it would bother me if it was called love. Like watering at the eyes or quivering at the glottis. That disgusts me. But let's leave it on one side for the moment, since I don't like talking about it. I say for the moment because I shall be willing to talk about it should the opportunity arise. I don't want to indulge my egotism. I want to do what has to be done. But I can already almost say that I shall instinctively see that the opportunity doesn't arise. And if that isn't honesty, then I don't what is.

Apropos of vomiting, it suddenly occurs to me, the need to vomit makes you salivate just like the need to eat or the other need that I don't want to talk about. An insignificant thing but bizarre, bizarre, it would quickly become monstrous if enlarged upon.

I've finished searching the garden, then, or I'm still searching it and have got to the gate. What happened there. Even if it doesn't come back to me just as it positively was, I'm sure that I looked over towards the other side, at the house opposite, that is, and the weathercock. Having yourself a weathercock made in the shape of a locomotive because you're a retired railroad man, that too is bizarre. Probably monstrous too, if enlarged upon. If *I* had retired from something, all I'd want to do would be to forget it. The thing is that this must have shocked me ever since I knew why the weathercock was that shape. This is certainly the reason for my lack of interest in that neighbour. Or one of the reasons in any case. Just imagining that we might talk to each other makes me salivate. And say what? I should immediately see that we don't have the same temperament. And even if I didn't see it immediately I should all the time be thinking about that weathercock, I wouldn't be able to say anything profound, anything heartfelt. Careful. Better leave it at that.

Well, here's what I was daydreaming about, I was imagining that I was trying to talk to the neighbour and that I was thinking about the weathercock and about our opposing temperaments and that I couldn't manage to get interested in him. And that I was racking my brains trying to find a way to forget the weathercock, to rise above it, and I couldn't manage it and I considered myself a total egoist and I disgusted myself. Temperament, temperament, that's not the only thing that exists after all, there are the fundamental qualities, perseverance, economy, moral hygiene, everything. I had no reason, under the pretext that he wasn't of my temperament, to deny him these qualities, to consider him a bastard. And as I didn't deny them to him, how could I refuse to talk with him? It was iniquitous. And in any case, what is temperament? Wanting to remember or to forget that you're retired? Without trying to be funny at all costs, isn't it perhaps something just as insignificant, which manifests itself in an equally insignificant fashion? Can we take that into account in refusing to make an acquaintance, let's simply say to open our mouths? Yes indeed we can! And how we can! Well, that's what dismays me. That's what I was thinking about, it must have been that. I would go further: by dint of trying to find a way to get into conversation with him, by dint of forcing myself to forget his temperament, I came up with the right ploy by chance. Chance, that's easy to say, we're all the time tempting it without meaning to. It's because we struggle that it comes, because we fight, because we badger ourselves. We ought rather to call it a miracle which crowns our efforts in an unexpected fashion, instead of the hat we were looking for we come across a saucepan lid and we're so fed up with searching that we tell ourselves it's a miracle, here's the saucepan lid I was looking for. It irritates me to come out with such an insipid explanation. I once developed a theory about chance and miracles but I don't remember what it was. I don't remember what I thought about them. It was something of this order but much more convincing. We go on believing that we still have the certainties we had when we were young but the day we want to lay our hands on them we can't find the right ploy. In short, miracle or chance, the way to do it dawned on me when I looked up at the scarecrow. The neighbour was at his gate, I was at ours, and I was trying to find a way to be friendly when all of a sudden the scarecrow gave me a helping hand. I said what a lovely scarecrow you have, did you make it yourself? The neighbour answered either yes or no, but the conversation had got going, I had overcome my repugnance. We chatted away nicely, quite relaxed, and I realized that my idea about temperament was all wrong, this man was very decent, all this time I had been depriving myself of a companion, of an outlet.

Or what if the scarecrow hadn't given me a helping hand? Or if I wasn't ready to take it and had gone on looking for a way? I have to know. In the first place, was the neighbour actually at his gate or was it that I walked over to the wall, just like that, having nothing better to do, and cast a surreptitious glance through the gate to see whether the neighbour was in his garden? That makes a difference. Me, casting surreptitious glances into other people's places! I didn't have anything better to do, true, but it was also out of curiosity. Or even out of compulsion? I took myself by the hand, I forced myself to make the leap into the dark, was the only interest I found in it that of torturing myself? A nature like mine which is always having to struggle has a great deal of difficulty in discovering with hindsight why it has done this or that. The very habit of struggling makes such a nature confuse its tastes with its duties. This must end either by disgusting you with struggling or by just quite simply disgusting you, and depriving you of your tastes. And without a minimum of tastes you might as well give up the ghost. I shall see, I shall see. Maybe, after all, I wasn't in the least trying to get into conversation with that cretin. Maybe I was on the contrary trying to persuade myself, to convince myself that it was impossible. I was looking for some other proof than the weathercock, I was glancing into the garden to pick up some detail, something really repugnant, a garden gnome for example. And did I find one?

All my wits. The hypotheses are all much the same but they don't lead to the same place. I'm forced to assume them, though, that's the only way I can recapture what I was thinking because I don't trust what comes back to me. I shouldn't have said I don't trust it. That'll only make things more of a shambles. One should assume the most plausible hypothesis but I have a feeling that that's where the difficulty lies. Actually, no one can say I'm fiddle-faddling, that I'm lapsing into the ludicrous as I did in the past. I'm still very down-to-earth, I'm not getting carried away. Well yes, that's where the difficulty lies. Every proposition is reasonable, at this level. That's the snag. There's a snag in everything but I'm going to have to get around it. Horribly afraid. If only I could be back in my former circumstances. When I used to tell the story of my life less self-consciously. On reflection, though, no. I mustn't regret it because even in those circumstances I didn't manage to rid myself of it. And now here I am, drawing a parallel between my former exposés and this one. They have nothing in common. I don't want to talk about my life, I want to find that paper.

Where was I. I was thinking about the neighbour, I was looking for a way. Did I find it? A garden gnome or something else, a hideous sun umbrella, a rockery, a Grecian vase, I don't know. I *must* know. I mustn't let myself be deluded by chimeras, I mustn't take my desires for realities. My desire to have done with the neighbour, in this instance. I have all the time in the world, I have my whole life. That's for sure. Solid grounds for a departure which really is one. And if my exposé is like the others, well, too bad. *I* shall know that it has nothing in common, that it's concrete, positive, practical, that I'm looking for that paper in it. This is a great concession on my part. An enormous concession. But after all, it's purely a matter of form. The content—I have the content in hand. If it tries to elude me, just make a note of the fact that I can already foresee that I shall make another concession but that I shall certainly find a way to get it back. It'll kill me but I shall find it. Fortunately, we haven't got there yet.

Let me think. A Grecian vase. A rockery. I lean on the gate, I examine the garden. On the right, the apricot trees and the scarecrow, on the left the house and its weathercock. But how stupid I am. This is still only a supposition. I'm supposing that I didn't want to talk to the neighbour. I must go back to my own, to our own, garden, to the moment when I got to the gate and started daydreaming. Was I really daydreaming? Wasn't it rather that I went out of the gate with my head lowered, still searching for the paper and that I only raised my head to see Marie at the window? That's one thing at least that has to be admitted, that she was at the window. And while the most important thing of all is to be conscientious, I repeat that I want to get ahead and that I refuse, is that the right word, that I don't want to be boring. I want to be a good companion. I can put myself in the place of people in my place, I know what it's like never to find the companion you need. A good, honest companion. And isn't that just the sort of companion who gives you a pain in the ass? I mustn't ask myself that question, it would wreck everything. I must hold on to, hang on to the idea that this particular companion is at least tolerable. Even if I don't really believe it, even if I'm forcing myself. I've no reason to be too afraid of relinquishing this idea. I'm used to forcing myself.

Next, Marie came down, she said trifle to me and I went on sitting on my chair. That was where I'd got to. Maybe that was where I'd got stuck. At the word trifle. I reviewed my whole life, I repacked my bag. I re-persuaded myself and I felt hungry and went into the kitchen. But I rather believe that I wasn't on my chair. I don't remember the movement, getting up from my chair and going into the kitchen. That too was a supposition, the business about the chair. What did I say, let me see now. That I had sat down on the chair to put Marie off the scent? Yes, it must have been that. But I was putting her off the scent in case she came down at the moment, so that she shouldn't catch me looking. Wasn't that it? So that was also a supposition, I wasn't really sure that she had come down, and if she had, then I told myself that it could only be Marie, whereas it might well have been someone else, who wasn't in the habit of humiliating me? What did I say? Do I have to remember everything I said? That's impossible. Even at this point, when I've only just begun my exposé, I am well aware that it's impossible. The genre doesn't oblige you to remember, it's a genre that's, how can I put it, living, vibrant, made of flesh and blood, I can't physically remember what I say at any given moment, I can't even remember what I did yesterday. Did all this happen yesterday, by the way? Yesterday or this morning? I don't remember. It happened, that's all that matters. No peroration about the weather. But then, where've I got to? Shit and re-shit.

Mustn't get worked up, mustn't let my mind wander. Let me repeat. I'm a decent fellow, a bit simple, rather small-scale. I founded as they say this guest house ten years ago with Gaston. We can still eat thanks to the guests, who pay. I'm an amateur botanist. From time to time I write an exposé of my life, to get rid of it, to be easy in my mind. What I'm doing at the moment is in a different, though related, genre. I say that I'm looking for a paper which I need for my botanical composition and I'm afraid that in this context I'll have to talk about my life, but if the opportunity arises I *will* talk about it, and in particular about the people I live with. That's simple,, isn't it? Does it make sense? Yes. The one and only thing that worries me is precision. Making a mountain out of that! But the mountain makes itself of its own accord, I observe that it makes itself of its own accord because all of a sudden I find myself facing it. My goodness, it isn't so very serious, let's walk around the mountain and carry on. And besides, it may well not be a mountain, I can't see very clearly, it's right in front of my nose. Barely a little hill, a little hummock, nothing at all. How nervous I am! We must calm down. A decent fellow, rather small-scale. It's scale that creates mountains, not decency. Has anyone ever talked about large-scale decency? Come on, come on. Let's start again calmly.

I got up at eight, I put on my dressing gown and went down to drink my tea in the refectory. Describe a piece of furniture, for a diversion. The sideboard. We bought it at an auction. We couldn't afford anything else so to console ourselves we told each other that it was funny, original. It's in two parts, like almost all sideboards. Its panels are carved. On the top ones, spaniels' heads in an oval. On the bottom ones, hunting trophies and vegetables. Partridges, kohlrabis, turnips. Along the hinges and all around them there's a torsade enhanced by two or three tooth-shaped mouldings, or maybe they're some other shape, I don't have it under my eyes. At the top, in the middle of the pediment, a kind of umbrella and waves rippling up to the corners which are surmounted by either funeral urns or boxes of tiddly-winks, a game we used to play in my day. In the drawers between the two parts, on the right there's the cutlery and on the left our guests' napkins. They stink, it's unbelievable. Makes you wonder how napkins, in which after all you don't secrete piles of carrion, can give off such a stench. It must be the same everywhere. In every necessitous household, I mean. Where you don't change the napkins every day. I have the sideboard in front of me, when I am at table. I drank my tea, then, and went upstairs again. I got dressed and sat down at my table. I wash in the evening. The hot water has to be brought up from the kitchen in a saucepan, you have to keep a tight hold of the basin while you're washing your feet and all the rest in it, it's exhausting. You don't feel like doing it all over again in the morning. And even if you did feel like it, there wouldn't be any water in the kitchen. In short, I sat down at my table, I read, I crossed out, I began again. After that I looked for the paper and went down into the garden, don't let's go over that again. I went the rounds of the garden, I didn't find anything. And something stopped me. If it was neither my thoughts about the neighbour nor Marie, and it doesn't seem as if it was, then it was something else. Let's carry on going the rounds of the garden, let's finish that in case I didn't finish it and then let's see. I pass the gate, I carry on up to the window of the salon, about ten meters. I said the craproom, we call it the craproom. It's what you might call our common room so we use that rather common expression, it's where we keep all the crap we use to entertain ourselves or to pass the time. Precise details will come later. I get to the window of the craproom. This is the only one on the left of the steps. The one on the right is that of the refectory. I've finished going the rounds, I haven't found anything, I'm about to raise my head, I do raise my head. That's it. This time it *is* coming back to me. I saw the chair under the chestnut tree, it was only at that moment that I saw it. I ought to have seen it a long time before. I wondered what it was doing there, we never took it out, it wasn't Mademoiselle Reber's chair. Well yes, I'm not avoiding her. She's the only person who sits in the garden a little in the summer. But her chair is red-varnished rattan, not one of the ugly little green ones, and we look after hers. Mademoiselle Reber gets angry when she finds any dust on it. We usually put it away in the shed in the evenings but we sometimes forget. We—I shall also have to say who that is. It's Fonfon. A simple-minded lad we took in to do the odd jobs. He only does them by halves but we keep him on just the same. We can't send him back to the carpentry shop we rescued him from at his mother's request. She was afraid he'd lose a finger or get his foot or his head crushed or everything at the same time. I've become attached to this Fonfon. That's a nickname, incidentally. His name is Gilles Fontaine. What a lot of precisions! I hope they aren't going to complicate things for me later on. Yes, I've become attached to him. The gentle eyes of an idiot, a thick-lipped mouth, tow-coloured hair, sleek and long. So it's his job to put away and take out Mademoiselle Reber's chair and to look after it, and wipe it. When the chair has been left out overnight by mistake, Mademoiselle Reber knows who to bawl out. This is convenient. Everyone in the guest house has his or her own function, we had to adopt this procedure to simplify our existence. He isn't a total idiot at that, he talks, he hits back, he says amusing things sometimes but even so he *is* simple-minded. A mental age of seven in a body of about fifteen. I don't even know how old he is. Neither does Gaston, nor anyone else, but this doesn't bother us. If we wanted to know we could always ask his mother. But what for? We aren't going to have to apply for a passport for the poor boy, for instance. He probably doesn't even have any identity papers, now I come to think of it. Do idiots have them? We

haven't declared him as an employee, of course, we give him a home,
that's all there is to it. But there must be some negligence on our part. In
case of a mishap, an accident, a fire, I don't know. And then, hell, that
isn't my department. Let Gaston get on with it. I'll talk to him about it
some time.

Yes, then I saw the chair and wondered what it was doing there, I
remember that exactly. Had Fonfon got the wrong chair? Surely not.
He's too afraid of getting a clout from Reber. Because she clouts him
when he isn't paying attention. She says that's the only way with idiots.
She's surely right. A dog or a cat, when you biff it over the muzzle, it
remembers what it mustn't do.

I went over to the chair, wiped it with a leaf, and sat down. Maybe I
wasn't thinking either of Marie or of the paper. Stuck with the chair. I
was already tired after my search, I couldn't care less about knowing
whether Marie was observing me or was just going to come down, and
as for the neighbour, no reason to think about him, I was letting my
mind wander. This still happens to me too frequently. I fight against it,
right, I'm used to it, that's true. But often, and I have to say this, I feel
I'm letting my mind wander and I don't react. I tell myself vaguely that
I'm packing my bag but I know very well that it's the opposite, I'm
unpacking it. I'm dissuading myself. After such moments I don't get
my strength back, nor the desire to eat. These are the true absences. It
starts a bit like the bag in the sense that you spy out the land but right
away everything starts going down instead of up. What are you thinking about? About your life, always. But you're no longer trying to
remedy it. Not me, at all events. I make a list of everything I lack, but
instead of filling in the gaps by moving something around I leave them
just as they are, I even widen them. Everything I lack, good God. And
everything I'm going to lack, perhaps even the taste for botany. What
shall I hang on to? To Gaston? To the guests? They wouldn't stand it for
long, they're half-putrefied. That has to be said, too. You can't live from
hand to mouth in squalor like that with impunity, when you have
nothing but sordid worries, stinking napkins, grease spots and mould.
You end up with a withered heart.

I have a feeling that mawkishness isn't far off so I won't go on. I'm
on my chair and I'm thinking about my life. Not say what I thought
about it. In any case, I'd like to point out to myself that it was only a
supposition. Perhaps I wasn't absent. I'd sat down because my foot hurt

and I needed to sit down. And once I was seated, I simply wondered what that chair was doing there. That's possible. Everything is possible. The price you have to pay for having no memory is heavy, heavy. To pay for what you don't have. That's all I've done ever since I've known myself. It's enough to make you want to scuttle your ship, I don't think that expression is too far-fetched. A fine ship. But who stuffed our heads full of these images? The people we saw in offices? Our reading matter? It must be our reading matter. If I had my life to live over again, as they say, I'd use all that reading matter to wipe myself with. I rather think I said in one of my exposés that every time I caught people reading I had them shot. It was a fantasy, it wasn't serious, but it said exactly what it meant to say. In short, even though those previous compositions weren't any use to me, I notice that I refer to them. Which means that I am no judge of their real usefulness. You have to be humble, humble. Sometimes accept that what isn't of any use may be of some use. I mean, accept that this is a possibility. We're still within the realm of hypothesis. *Are* we still there? I need to know where that paper is. I shall always come back to that.

So on the chair to have a rest. I couldn't have known why the chair was there, I can't have thought about it for very long. Let's say until twenty to ten. Impossible not to mention Marie at this moment, she must inevitably have come down, it was time for her to go shopping. And impossible too that she didn't ask me what I was doing on that chair. If I answered in an aggressive tone of voice, we know what follows. And if I didn't, we also know it. That's to say, no. If my tone was not aggressive, I stayed on the chair, but for how long? If I did, in view of the effort I had to put into resurfacing after the trifle, I undoubtedly went into the kitchen. I opt for the kitchen.

One more thing. I'm writing this just the way it comes, the way you speak, the way you perspire. When I say that I don't remember what I've said, it's true, but I ought to say wrote. If I wanted to I could reread it but that doesn't interest me. I don't mind if I contradict myself. What's said is never said because you can say it differently.

One more thing while I'm about it. I don't know why I'm thinking of it at this moment. I have nothing against lust. It suits a lot of people and they're lucky. But not me. It depresses me and what's more I lose my head. It's when I'm lying down that my imagination starts working overtime in that direction and I run the risk of returning to the path of what is called pleasure. But I need to keep my head, in order to find that paper. I'm going to have to remain standing up as much as possible. Or sitting down, of course.

I went into the kitchen to get something to eat. There was no one there, the cook is on holiday. It's July. Most of the guests are on holiday too. They go off to stay with their nieces in general and to recharge their batteries a little before coming back to our régime in September. But even if they were better fed with us, they'd still go on holiday. it gives them something else to think about, they say. I can't say they come back with any new thoughts but that's their affair. I opened the cupboard then, and took out the remains of a loaf of bread and some cheese. I open the cupboard, I take the loaf, I cut myself a slice, I look for the cheese on the right hand side of the middle shelf. It's coming back to me. There wasn't any cheese. Gaston told Marie last night not to forget the cheese, she'll have added it to her list. Did I look for anything else in the kitchen? Some mustard to put on my bread? A tomato? No. I went into the refectory, the breakfast things hadn't been cleared away. I go into the refectory. Windows wide open. Ghastly July light. Flies everywhere, on the butter, on the jam, on the oilcloth. The smell of burned fat already coming from the canteen next door. I take some jam and spread it on my bread. It's apple jelly, either lemon or raspberry flavoured. More of a raspberry colour. Does Madame Sougneau really put raspberries in it? Madame Sougneau is the cook. Some sort of flavouring essence? In any case, something that doesn't cost much. Apple jelly is the most economical. The neighbours have given us permission to collect all the uneatable windfalls under their apple trees in the autumn and we treat ourselves to this jelly all year long. Madame Sougneau has some very big jam pots and some smaller ones. If we start on a big one we have to finish it first before we open another. So sometimes either the lemon or the raspberry lasts and lasts, we'd love to have a change but there's nothing doing. I took some jam. Lemon? Yes, it's lemon at the moment. Didn't Fonfon just ask if we could have a change? This morning? No, yesterday. Who told him no? It was Marie. She came in just at that moment, she interrupted me. I was going to say something less curt, something like you know very well we can't, just be patient for another week, she said nothing doing and Fonfon shut his trap. People who have never lived frugally, having to count every sou, don't realize how horrible it is. The slightest little desire for the least little thing is a luxury, you have to stifle it. You spend your whole time stifling things. Not surprising that you get squashed flat, that you shrivel. You only have to look at our guests. They may well, some of them, have a big stomach or big breasts, but they're as flat as a pancake. Morally speaking, I mean. I sometimes wonder whether some sort of gadgets don't exist that can test people's morale. What with the improvements in technology and psychology, they ought to exist. It must be appalling to consult their gauges or dials or photos. In our cases. All those stifled desires, all those aspirations nipped in he bud. And hope turns into something like a compact little stump, something like chewing-gum.

Or was I the one who told Marie not to forget the cheese? To put up a bold front, to stave off the word trifle? Impossible to remember. I must. I was searching, I must have been near the gate. I hear Marie coming downstairs, I tell myself let's put a bold front on it. She comes out on to the steps. I look up and say don't forget the cheese, some blue and some gruỳere. That may be it. Some blue and some gruỳere. No point in getting any blue, she says, Madame Cointet's away and you don't eat it, nor does Monsieur Gaston. I said it isn't only Madame Cointet, there's Mademoiselle Reber. Reply: oh, her. No one likes Mademoiselle Reber, she gets on everybody's nerves with her orderliness and her obsessions. Did Marie reply that? In any case I would have said buy some in any case. She comes down the steps, she passes quite near me and to get her own back she adds, *now* what are you looking for. Did she say that? I don't think I'd have been able to avoid it. Unless I didn't happen to be near her at that moment? Perhaps still near the shed? Buy some in any case. Oh, her. She goes out of the gate, she buggers off. That's it. She didn't say anything else, she simply buggered off. I was by the shed, I'd just searched it, I was in there longer than I said just now. I went on searching the garden after Marie had gone. In other words, I didn't need to go into the kitchen.

Let's start again. I walked along the wall, looking in the shrubbery. It isn't a shrubbery, it's a hedge in front of the party wall between us and our neighbours, the Rivoires. Their villa is just behind it, when I'm in my room I look down on to the veranda on their ground floor, which has blue and yellow glass. I know absolutely nothing about the Rivoires, I've never tried to find out who they are. I don't even know why our guests never talk about them. Do they only live there for part of the year? Are they legless cripples? Have they been dead for years? If I have to find out for the sake of that paper, we'll see. Along the hedge, then.

Next, the gate. Did I perhaps cast a surreptitious glance into the street to see if I could still see Marie at the far end? No reason. Or look in the street to see if the paper was there? Obviously I looked. I even went out of the garden but I didn't go far. Of that I am sure. I don't want the neighbours to know that I'm always looking for something. I haven't said that yet. If it isn't a bit of paper it's something else. It's quite enough for me to cope with Marie's and some of the guests' insults without courting them from the neighbours. Forever looking for something! I've tried to change my ways, to concentrate on everything I do, the result was nil. I probably went about it the wrong way. It looks as if it even deprived me of what little memory I had when I was young.

I looked in the street, I certainly looked up at the house opposite. Did I go as far as its gate? I definitely don't think so. The weathercock and the scarecrow, that was another day. I didn't imagine that I tried to talk to the neighbour, that was another day. Or maybe after, after I was back in our own garden? Our own garden! Anyone who saw it would laugh at me. And that chestnut tree. At the very beginning it was still intact, it was only later that they extended the cables. I must say that truncated or not we'd have moved in just the same, given the price of the dump. What a job, good God! When we had to change the central heating boiler, put new washers everywhere, all the pipes starting to leak, bits of the floor rotting under the lino, new lino to buy, all the redecoration, I always say to Gaston, can you believe how young we were. Maybe say a word about Gaston. He was an old school friend. We met again by chance ten years later at Sirancy where he was taking the waters. I was just passing through, he was taking a cure for an intestinal complaint. We met in the park one evening, me between two drinking bouts, him between two bouts of diarrhea. And we refraternized immediately, and almost immediately we pooled our savings for his guest house project. In short, now I come to think of it, our two existences are founded on a history of caca. Here, I can't avoid it. It's so stupid, so vulgar. Mind you, I hadn't the slightest aptitude for anything whatsoever. I was struggling along as best I could, I was fed up with myself, I thought it would be a solution. And that's it. Poor Gaston. He thought he was going to make his fortune, that I was going to back him up, give him some ideas, shake him up a bit. At the beginning I'm not saying I didn't, with all those repairs, I certainly did what I could, but afterwards. And what's more, he never got rid of his intestinal troubles. Even after re-taking the cure. I used to joke about it in the past. I told him go and re-take your cure but whatever you do don't talk to anyone. So he wouldn't go and bring us back another crackpot and new projects. We'd have been in a nice mess.

I went back into the garden and continued on my round. I came to the craproom window. It must have been at that moment that I looked up at the chestnut tree. Not to see the nest, to find my paper. Caught in a branch, you never know. Or was Fonfon in the chestnut tree? I've forbidden him to climb it, he might hurt himself, but it's a waste of breath. Was Fonfon in the chestnut tree. Could he have climbed it while I was in the street? Let me think. I'm in the street. Do I hear anything. No. Why. Because I'm only thinking about my paper. But what if I was thinking about the neighbour, telling myself let's not think about him this time, let's concentrate on that paper? I can't possibly not have looked up at the weathercock and said to myself that stupid fool of a neighbour, and I can't possibly not have seen the scarecrow and told myself the same thing. Well, that's enough. That stupid fool of a neighbour twice. But I'd be surprised if I didn't say something else to myself. Either no danger of my talking to him, or else the contrary. Maybe the contrary. Not to torture myself, merely to ask him whether he hadn't by any chance seen a paper fluttering by. Just like that, casually. In which case I'd still be in the street, I'd be going over towards his gate. I go over. I glance into the garden. The neighbour isn't there. Didn't I try to call him? No. I must have told myself that I'd ask him sometime whether he hadn't seen a bit of paper fluttering by. Sometime? Impossible. I had to know right away. I may perhaps have told myself that if I didn't find it at our place I'd go back and see whether the neighbour was in his garden, adding that stupid fool with his weathercock and his scarecrow, he certainly won't have seen anything, he's so intent on his obsessions, his horrors, a bit of paper would leave him completely cold. But what if, on the other hand, he couldn't bear to see a bit of paper in his garden path? If in fact he'd picked mine up and thrown it into his ghastly garbage can in the shape of a tree trunk? A garbage can in the shape of a tree trunk! Authentic. A stump, rather, made of cement, with the cracks of the bark and the knots of the wood. He sees this paper in his garden path, he bends down, he puts it in his garbage can. That's what I was thinking. I was seeing him in the act of throwing my paper away. I had to speak to him. When I'd finished my round of our garden. I'd go back to his gate and I'd talk to him. Opening remarks, the fine weather, the sun, the birds. Too many birds. I understand you with your scarecrow. Did you make it yourself? That's it, that's right. Unless it was a bird that took my paper. Idiot.

I went back into our garden, carried on with my search and got to the craproom window. I looked up at the chestnut tree. Was Fonfon in it, yes or no, hell. Careful. I don't know. He's up there all the time, even though I've forbidden it. I have to know.

What drudgery I've let myself in for in writing this. To have to re-immerse myself in that nauseating morning, in all those nauseating mornings, and afternoons, and evenings, and all the rest. But I can't do anything else. I didn't let myself in for anything, it imposed itself. I can't continue my work without that paper and I have to say so. Try to understand me, try to put yourself in my place. I wonder whether anyone would want to. Anyone.

Fonfon wasn't in the chestnut tree. I looked up for the paper, telling myself that it was useless but let's look just the same. And while I was looking I may well have thought that Fonfon must have climbed it a few moments before, just before I went down into the garden, and that he'd seen my paper stuck between two leaves and picked it up and thrown it away. Or that he hadn't picked it up? In which case, wouldn't I see it, there, now? Nothing. I didn't see anything in the chestnut tree. But this idea of Fonfon gives me an idea. Let's quite calmly go back to the beginning.

I got up at eight, having been woken by Marie. She knocks on my door three times. If I don't grunt she knocks again until I do grunt. Impossible to talk in the morning. Even yes upsets me. Especially yes. I got up, I put on my dressing gown. An old dressing gown, always the same one, made of brown material with yellow collar and cuffs. I've lost the belt. Let's hope I don't have to look for it. It's not impossible that before I went downstairs to drink my tea I looked out of the window. Not to see anything, but because I'd heard Fonfon singing under his breath. He usually does that when he's going to do some damn silly thing. That must be it. I looked out of the window and saw him making his way towards the shed. Did I ask him what he was doing? No. I waited for him to take out Mademoiselle Reber's chair. He took it out. I waited a bit longer. What I'm saying here is very difficult to remember because this happens every day. I mustn't mix up the different times. He went back to the shed and I told myself that he was waiting for me to disappear and then he's going to climb the chestnut tree. But maybe that wasn't his intention. In any case he didn't come out right away and I went downstairs. Did I pass anyone in the corridor or on the stairs? The only people left in the guest house at the moment are Gaston and me, Mademoiselle Reber and Madame Apostolos. Mademoiselle Reber spends the summer with us and some years she goes to her niece in September, in Alsace. Every time she comes back she regales us with the same stories about storks, sauerkraut, and first communions. The granddaughter of one of her school friends who made hers in the spring, or her great-nephew who got indigestion after eating sausages, or the storks which didn't return to such and such a place. This doesn't interest anyone but it keeps the conversation going in the evenings, like everything the rest of them say about their holidays. Maybe the only reason they go away is to have something to talk about when they come back? They'd do better not to go. But that would mortify them. As for me, I let them talk, I haven't actually listened for ages, I mix up all the nieces, they're always reproaching me about it. Did I pass Reber? She comes down at that time to drink her coffee and then goes back up to her room until ten o'clock. If I did meet her she could only have been going downstairs and we must have gone down together. If I passed Madame Apostolos she could only have been either coming back from or going to the bog. It's at the other end of the corridor. She goes there all the time, all night, she stops some people sleeping with the noise she makes pulling the chain. She won't use her chamber pot, it's infuriating. I don't hear anything myself, I'm on the second floor. I don't know if she goes there to annoy the others or because she needs to or because she thinks she needs to. In any case as everyone knows she steals the bog paper. No one knows what she does with it. She always has a packet of it in her peignoir pocket when she comes back from the bog. It's a very delicate matter for Gaston to tell her to stop it on account of the expense. Or if he has told her, she still does it. She's a strange old girl, Madame Apostolos. She's always been a refugee, we've lost track of which war or which catastrophe. Our third guest, I rather think. Or our fourth. Or our second? I don' remember. She still pretends to some kind of elegance in spite of the fact that she obviously hasn't a bean. She must dye her hair herself. Red. And she paints her mouth violet. Or vice versa. It's so glaring and so ugly that it hurts your eyes. In the summer, short-sleeved flowered dresses, you can see her poor old arms, all flabby, all white. But it's her legs that are the most pitiful sight. Covered in blue varicose veins, a real dish of macaroni on each. She's rheumaticky, she limps, and some days she can only just manage to drag herself upstairs. She has a canary which she keeps in her room and stuffs with semolina. She says that the atmosphere of the guest house deprives it of its urge to sing but it must be the semolina. Yes, it was Apostolos I passed. She was coming back from the bog. I must have said good morning to her. Was she coming back or was she going? If she was going I wouldn't have needed to say good morning to her, if she'd got beyond the stair well. I hope I make myself clear without having to do a drawing of it. The staircase is in the middle of the corridor and I was just coming down to the first floor. She was coming back, quite so, and she'd already passed the stair well. She had her back to me, I didn't see her bulging pocket, I must have told myself, there's another half packet slipping through our fingers. I didn't ask her any questions because I wasn't yet aware that I'd lost my paper. Right, I went down to the refectory. And I was with Reber in the refectory, we were together at the table. She has white hair scraped back into a bun, she wears little gold spectacles and a grey dress. Shoes that I believe are called Oxfords. Less deformed at the big toe than those of Madame Apostolos. This deformation disgusts me. I try not to think about it but it's always what I look at. At this moment Mademoiselle Reber's feet are under the table, she's drinking her coffee. She tells me she probably won't be going to visit her niece this year. Yes, this must have been the first time she told me so that day. She told me again later but I was thinking about the paper and I mixed it up with what Apostolos had told me about *her* niece. But it's not important, I'm only talking about it so as to get my bearings. And to remind myself of something about Fonfon. That was it. I was looking out of the window while Reber was telling me all that stuff and I saw Fonfon coming out of the shed but he didn't go over to the chestnut tree. I must have told myself that he was feinting again. Next I went upstairs to dress. Didn't I pass Marie on the stairs? I did. Maybe I even told her then not to forget the cheese, and repeated it later in the garden. With her you have to repeat everything three or four times.

I went into my bedroom which is on the second floor, I repeat. With Gaston's room and the one the maids share and a very small one, more of a cubby hole, for Fonfon's bed. The bed is good even if the room isn't. He's pinned a picture of the Sacred Heart above it and a photo of a coal-tit cut out of a magazine. My own room isn't big either but it does have running water, a washbasin on the left as you go in, then comes the wardrobe, then the window. On the right, my table and my bed. I immediately missed the paper. First I searched under all the furniture, then I looked out of the window and told myself that the paper might have blown away. Was it at that moment that I saw Fonfon in the chestnut tree? That's it, this time it's coming back to me. I didn't see him. I went down, searched the garden, and went up again, and when I was back upstairs I looked out of the window again, I thought it was odd for Fonfon to wait such a long time, and in fact I saw him climbing the tree. He had no idea that I was still watching him. If I shouted to him to come down it might frighten him and make him fall, so I went downstairs yet again. I was all ready to speak in a soft but firm voice, and get him to understand that he had to come down. I may even have found a pretext, that's the best way with him. I was going to tell him to go and count how many bottles there were left in the cellar. He likes being given responsibilities. When I got to the chestnut tree, no Fonfon. He must have heard me coming down. Heard me talking to Apostolos or Reber? No, I was in a hurry to get out into the garden again. This time I called him, he could only be in the shed. He didn't answer, I went and looked, he wasn't there either. But he often disappears, there was no cause for alarm.

All this has just come back to me en bloc, that's fine but it meant I had to make two trips into the garden, what a bore. The first one, let's say that I did what I said I did and that Marie went shopping. On to the second one, now. I looked into the street to see if I could see Fonfon and it was only then that I started daydreaming about the weathercock, the scarecrow and all the rest. That seems more likely. Not being able to find the paper in the garden, in one sense my mind was more at liberty, so I started daydreaming. Then I went upstairs again. And it was while I was going upstairs that I passed Madame Apostolos on her way back from the bog. It's becoming clearer all the time. I said good morning to her, I saw her bulging pocket and I made an association with my own paper. I asked her whether she hadn't seen it. She asked me what sort of paper. I said with a botanical note, a bit of white paper, maybe an eighth of a sheet. She hadn't seen anything but I thought the way she answered me was rather odd. I must be on my guard against my impressions, I'm always telling myself that, it can become serious if I exaggerate, I shall end up suspecting everyone and getting ideas into my head and I don't want that. But it's very difficult to fight against. You get carried away in spite of yourself, you start embroidering, you get worked up, and the net result is that you can't sleep. When this happens to me, I mean when

I can't sleep, I tell myself again that I'm a decent fellow, on a rather small scale. That's my way of counting sheep. It usually soothes me. But the day when it no longer soothes me? I'm afraid, and I go on being afraid. Keep calm, keep calm.

Unless I had my tea with Reber and only passed her on the stairs the second time I went up? That's possible, she always hangs around in the refectory, I believe she helps herself to another slice of bread and butter, she's always going on about people who eat too much, she finishes her meal behind our backs. And I don't think I saw her twice, first in the refectory and then on the stairs. I must have seen her at that moment, I said good morning to her and automatically asked her if she hadn't seen my paper. Just a tiny little botanical note, on an eighth of a sheet of paper. She said no but in a different way, a way that implied my poor friend, you'll always be the same. I don't like that either. To change the subject she must have told me that Fonfon hadn't taken her chair out. I'd just seen him taking it out. She said see for yourself. I went down a few steps, looked into the garden through the open door and saw that the red chair wasn't there. I was sure I'd seen Fonfon from my room taking out the red chair. Had he taken it out and then put it back again. Reber told me not to worry, she'd take it out herself but he'd get his clout, you can be sure of that. I must certainly have told her not to clout him too much, she must certainly have said with idiots that's the only way.

I wonder whether I'm right to describe everything in such detail. Yes, I am right. But it's going to become insipid. And yet I have to find that paper. I'm already beginning to wonder whether I really did come down twice. I have to be on my guard against things that come back to me too easily. It would be better to start again. Calmly. Very calmly. As if I was talking about something else, or better still about someone else, so as not to get edgy. Let's try to relax.

I got up at eight, having been woken by Marie. I put on my dressing gown and went down to drink my tea in the refectory. I may have passed Apostolos though I can't be sure, I may have had my tea with Reber though I can't be sure. That's too easy. I have to be sure. I have to shoulder my responsibilities. All my wits. I sit down in my place. I pick up the teapot, I pour myself out a cup. I add sugar and milk. I stir. I wait a moment until it isn't quite so hot, and look out of the window. Hideous light, the Rivoires' wall, truncated chestnut tree, shed. In actual fact, all I can see from my place is the chestnut tree and part of the wall, I imagine the rest without meaning to. The picture completes itself. Swallows were swooping around in the inferno, I could hear them. Even at my age they still cut me to the heart, I'm not exaggerating. They seem to me to be proclaiming the joy I never had. If I was on my own, I'd keep all the windows closed in July. I'd stifle, but at least I'd know why. I could also catch the smell of burned fat and I said that smell makes me feel sick, don't you think we should close the window? Yes, there was definitely someone with me. It could only have been Reber, Madame Apostolos comes down later. Or Gaston? Or even Marie? Maybe Marie, quite simply. She was still setting the table or she was bringing the coffee, the milk, all the stuff. And that butter already melted on the plate, which makes me feel sick. We'd love to have a fridge, but that... Gaston would rather spend the money on a washing machine first. I shall have an opportunity to come back to that. Quite simply Marie. Don't you think we should close the window? She replied with this heat, what an idea, it gives us a bit of air in the kitchen, we'd stifle otherwise. That nauseating smell of burned fat. If I had any sense I'd say that everything was nauseating. This guest house for down-and-outs, these worries, these conversations, these holiday departures, these returns. But that may simply be my own point of view because they don't seem to suffer so much. The holidays, for instance, you'd almost think they look forward to them. They start talking about them in January, if not before. I could understand it if they sometimes went somewhere else, but for their whole life those nieces, that's nauseating, isn't it? Apparently not. Madame Sougneau, now, who's just told me that she's going to stay with her niece, as if I didn't know it, and that she was taking her a little present, and she showed it to me, and she was smiling, she looked pleased. Exactly like last year. Poor Madame Sougneau. She's a widow. She has a daughter somewhere, she never talks about her, according to Gaston she's a streetwalker. In the evenings after they've finished the dishes the maids chat in the refectory while we bore ourselves to death in the craproom. This is the good moment in their day. Around ten they go up to their room which is much the same as mine. Above the beds, in the middle if you like, there's a picture of the Sacred Heart, plus Saint Anthony, plus the Angel of Judgment. Above the sewing machine, a rosary made out of big triangular seeds draped around the photo of the late Sougneau. Drooping moustache, cross-eyed, maybe on account of being touched up. His widow sews on Sundays. The seeds—I don't know what they are. Both she and Marie get their clothes from the Magasins-Prix. They buy much the same sort of thing. In summer a black silk coat, a black straw hat, a black dress with white polka dots. Obviously they don't buy new clothes every year. One summer, for instance, they'll put a new collar on a dress, the next summer it'll be a new ribbon on a hat, and so on and so forth. That's what they discuss in the evenings. Madame Sougneau went on holiday the other day with new shoes that hurt her feet. Marie advised her to take the old ones with her in her suitcase as well as her bedroom slippers. Fonfon wanted to be allowed to put her suitcase in the bus, under my supervision. The bus stops right outside our gate, it's most convenient. Ten past eight and ten past two in one direction, twenty to twelve and twenty to seven in the other. The eight o'clock one goes to Agapa, the two o'clock one to Douves. I'm just saying that for a bit of light relief. I'm still at my tea with Marie. She went back into the kitchen to fetch the milk and coffee. She put them down on the table. She looked out of the window and said what's that idiot doing. Fonfon was bringing out one of the little green chairs. I said to Marie no don't say anything to him, let him do it his own way, we mustn't find fault with him all the time, we shall see. So he really had taken it out, I hadn't been dreaming.

I'm going to have to make a slight change in the way I tell things. I can't keep saying probably or maybe, it's boring and it doesn't do any good. Once people realize that I write the way I talk to myself they're forewarned. I can't forewarn them of surprises and contradictions, because I've embarked on a voyage of discovery. I'm also obliged to make suppositions but I don't want to emphasize that too much, it might seem irresponsible, and yet it's one of the things that can help me the most. In any case you can rely on my conscientiousness, I shan't suppose just anything, always what's most plausible. And I mustn't make any more excuses for myself now, what I'm doing isn't easy, I have a lot at stake.

I saw Fonfon, then, putting the green chair under the chestnut tree and I said to myself God knows what stupid thing he's cooking up this time, I'll have to deal with it myself to save him from getting clouted. Next Marie opened the doors of the sideboard and put the dishes away. She told me there were only three bottles left in the cellar, we must order some more nine degrees proof, would I please tell Gaston. I thought back to our recent discovery of nine degrees wine, we used to buy the eleven degrees, that represents a nice savings at the end of the year. I mustn't forget to tell Gaston, he does the ordering by telephone. When I saw the bottom of the sideboard open I also thought about the liqueurs Gaston used to make in the days when he still had ideas. Cacao, blackcurrant, raspberry. That was at the very beginning, when we still indulged in extravagances. These days we've got the message. Besides, the liqueurs were undrinkable, we used to force ourselves to believe they were good. I drank my tea and went upstairs. Mademoiselle Reber passed me on the stairs and I asked her whether she had slept well, she said no, Madame Apostolos pulled the chain four times, I couldn't get back to sleep. But that was as usual and Mademoiselle Reber is slightly deaf, I'm sure she can't hear anything at the other end of the corridor. Maybe she hears Apostolos going out of her room which is opposite her own and immediately imagines the noise the chain makes? I honestly don't believe that either. She says she can't sleep like a lot of people who don't want to seem as if they do, no one knows why. There's nothing to be ashamed of in sleeping. If there was I'd have to die of shame, because I can sleep a good twelve hours. In short, that's what she told me and I went up to my room. I looked out of the window to see what Fonfon was doing. Did I see him bring out the red chair as well? I shall have to ask him quite simply whether or not he took it out. Wine and chair. Mustn't forget, wine and chair. I got dressed. And I sat down at my table. A lot could be said about the movement you make every day when you sit down at your work table. It gives you a kind of comforting feeling because you know that botany, at least, is something that won't escape you like all the rest, and at the same time you feel a kind of shame because you know very well that you're a coward to have refused to live like everyone else. But I've already said why I refused. Even so, it still bothers me. However much I say that the others bore me, I know they're worth more than me and my botany. How do I know it? Why? Because. Courage. I sat down at my table, read over what I'd written yesterday, crossed it all out and began again. I say yesterday again even though I'm not all that sure. When I'm sure I'll say the day before. Right away I missed my paper. I looked on the table, in the little card index, between the pages of the manuscript, under the blotting paper, then all over the room, under all the furniture, that's to say the table, the wardrobe and the bed, under the bedside mat. I didn't go so far as to take up the lino, we mustn't exaggerate, even though this certainly crossed my mind. I also wondered whether Marie had found the paper and automatically screwed it up into a little ball and then either swept it up with the dust, or irritably thrown it under the washbasin, or more likely out of the window. Here at last is the reason why I went down into the garden. The paper blowing away in the wind, sure, that's always possible, but the little ball is even more so. A ball. I can see Marie throwing that ball away. Don't tell me that my meticulousness is pointless, it's suddenly shown me something I haven't so far thought about. Thought about saying, I mean. Something I haven't yet remembered I'd thought about. The most important thing, even, the one that's crystal-clear. I looked out of the window, thinking about the paper blowing away, and that for the ball I had to go down in any case. That's what made me go down. I could almost see the paper from upstairs. So I went down.

I passed Madame Apostolos in the corridor. She'd just come out of the bog. I had a front view of her and her bulging pocket. I'm certain that I said to myself there's another lot slipping through our fingers. I said good morning did you sleep well. She replied that in this heat her rheumatism played her up. Did she say humid heat? In any case she was limping no end. She may have told me that her canary couldn't sleep, that's possible. Can a canary suffer from insomnia? She must be imagining things or else she dreams that her canary can't sleep. What can she dream about, poor woman? At her age can the memory of pleasure come back to her? In any case, displeasure must come back, troubles, moves, money matters, the dead. The canary, too. I've never seen it since the day she arrived, I never go into the guests' rooms. Maybe it isn't the same one as it was at first? Could she have bought herself another? I don't remember her saying anything about it. Ask Gaston. Wine and Apostolos canary. I went down into the garden. And in fact, there was the little green chair and not the red one. I told myself that I'd ask Fonfon after I'd searched the garden for my paper ball. Or did I ask him before? Before. I said let's get rid of that before, so he doesn't get himself slapped later. I called him. No answer. I went to the shed, he wasn't there. On the other hand, the red chair *was* there. I called a second time, went over to the gate and looked in the street, I couldn't see him. Nothing to worry about, this happens all the time. I don't know what he does, he probably goes to the other end of the village. Or down to the river? I've no idea. I can't even begin to imagine what he does, his poor brain probably doesn't know either. What I should have done was take out the red chair myself. Why didn't I think of it? Why didn't I do it? Either I thought Reber wouldn't come down before

Fonfon came back, or I couldn't wait to find my paper ball. Bizarre. Or did I imagine that Fonfon had crossed the road and gone into the garden opposite? Does he go there? Does he know the neighbour? It's not impossible that I indulged in a little daydreaming about that while I was looking at the scarecrow. If Fonfon knows the neighbour that's a good opening remark. Say to the neighbour for example I hope our poor lad doesn't importune you. Say importune, that sounds cultured. So he doesn't take me for just anyone, so he's aware of the distance. The stupid fool. It's so true, when you're all the time trying to abolish distances you don't do yourself any more good than you do the others. They think you're one of them for five minutes but you can't keep it up any longer than that and then, well, you're up shit creek. The other realizes he's made a mistake, he changes his tone, he closes up, he starts blathering, and for our part we don't know how to get out of it, we despise ourselves, we tell ourselves that we shouldn't have started that way, it was dishonest, we try to patch it up while we go on talking but all the time thinking we mustn't use this or that word so as not to disconcert him, in no time at all you've lost all track of what you were saying, you've wrecked the whole thing, it's intolerable. Mark out the distances right from the start. Say importune. Doesn't our poor child importune you? Not in the least, Monsieur, he says Monsieur, not in the least, he plays with the cat, ah, you have a cat? That's it, the conversation has started, has got off to a good start, on the appropriate level. The tone is there. The tone. The most difficult thing to capture. Your whole life can be messed up by a wrong tone. It's terrifying when you come to think of it. More than terrifying. Mortal. And we sometimes wonder what people die of. We can't explain it, we don't understand, we say it's a mystery. It's their tone that has killed them. They didn't pick the right one at the start. The tone. It's vital.

He plays with the cat. You have a cat? I might prolong the conversation to find out what he thinks of Fonfon. He doesn't find him insufferable since he doesn't stop him playing with his cat. Does he think him a total idiot, totally incurable? That he won't ever be any better? I'm always thinking about Fonfon. We took him in and I became attached to him. To his eyes or to his mouth or to his hair, but do I take enough interest in his soul, in his poor baby's soul? Do I take enough pains with him? Oughtn't I to get him to read? You know what I think about reading matter but in Fonfon's case if it would help him to develop I would give him reading lessons, I'd go as far as that. But it would tire him. Maybe the neighbour could give me his opinion? Especially if he's stupid? I've so often noticed that intelligent people give only bad advice, they make a shambles of everything. But this goes back to my office memories. Fortunately, there's no conspicuous intelligence in the guest house. Which doesn't stop them having no opinion of Fonfon. Or rather, they have no great opinion of him. That's one more reason to get into contact with the neighbour. That's what I was thinking about when I saw the scarecrow and the weathercock. After that I started searching the garden. I had to stoop quite a bit, a paper ball can easily get lost in the gravel. For we have some gravel. Not much, but some. Every so often I ask Fonfon to rake it over towards the wall and the gate, or to dig it out after heavy rain, for instance. It always sinks in on that side. So that the neighbours shouldn't say we let everything go to rack and ruin. It's stupid because I don't give a damn about the neighbours. So I was stooping forward quite a bit. I started my round at the steps, to do things systematically. The flower-bed. The slope leading down to the cellar. Can you see the route? Can you locate it? When you come in from the street and stop at the gate you have the garden in front of you, in the middle there's the chestnut tree, at the far end the shed. On the right, the Rivoire wall, on the left, the house. It has an upper floor plus the attic floor under the roof, which makes two. The steps are in the center of the facade. On the left, the craproom window, on the right that of the refectory. The slope leading down to the cellar is in the far corner after the refectory window. When I can be bothered I'll describe the interior. It contains quite a few nauseating things which would soon make people disgusted with objects. Objects! To come to the point. The slope leading down to the cellar. I went a little way down it, the ball might be by the door. It isn't impossible that the door had been left open, Marie never closes it. We're always telling her to close it but she just can't seem to remember. She says when you think what there is in it to steal. That's true, but it's the principle. I must have gone in. Telling myself that the ball had taken advantage if I can so put it of the door being open. I looked in the pile of coal on the right, in the potatoes on the left, in the bottle rack at the far end. I must certainly have seen that there were only three bottles left, though I can't remember if I thought about it. Above the rack, an enormous nail which we've never removed but which frightens me. I'm always thinking that anyone could hang himself from it. It isn't precisely above the rack, it's to the right, his feet wouldn't touch the ground, barely a piece of coal. There was nothing in the cellar. I had to stay there a long time, you can hardly see a thing, the bulb is far too dim. I came out and locked the door. Big key which we never take out of the lock. Next along the shed side, which is also that of the factory. There's a wall there too, covered in ivy. From the wall I zigzagged over about a third of the garden. I told myself that I'd do the third third, on the gate side, next, and the second, the middle one, last of all. That's where the chestnut tree is. Nothing. I went into the shed, I said that at the beginning. But I stayed there longer than I said just now. You can hardly see a thing in there either even though there is a window, or let's call it a chink, and the door is left open. That door has always got on my nerves. We never shut it either and on windy nights it bangs like all doors do though maybe it makes a different noise because the lintel has half rotted away and I reinforced it with a plank that doesn't fit properly, and that creaks too. I don't dare act the cop in the shed because it's Fonfon who goes there the most. Next from the shed to the Rivoire wall. Next along the Rivoire wall, only because of the aucubas, I'd deal with the third third after. Nothing in the aucubas. It's a horrible plant with sickly yellow patches all over it, we'd have been well advised to replace it right from the start. They say it remains green in the winter but actually it remains sickly yellow. And when its fruits appear, the odd red berry here or there, it's even uglier. When I got to the gate I stopped, opened it and looked out into the street. I stayed there too longer than I said just now. The ball might be jammed up against the sidewalk or even have drifted away in the gutter. In that case there was nothing more I could do. How far along the street did I go? Maybe twenty meters. In only one direction, downwards, that I do remember. I never go up in the street to the little square, I don't know why. I ought to know. Probably an unpleasant memory attached to that side, I'd rather not try too hard to remember. There are places like that in the village where I never go. Not that I go out a lot but there are some. Even when I go herborizing in the woods I avoid a certain path. What I call unpleasant memories are a whole lot of things that would seem ludicrous to anyone who wasn't in the know. Either a different quality of light, it's different everywhere, or the memory of an embarrassing or sad situation I'd found myself in and which a certain place reminds me of, I don't know why, probably nothing at all to do with the sad memory. Like the echo of a malaise. There too I ought to try to find the connection for every place I avoid but there'd be no end to it and it wouldn't make any difference, I should still avoid it. On the whole, I blame everything on the light, that simplifies matters. When I have to explain, I mean,. To Gaston, or to anyone else. I say that I prefer to go another way because of the quality of the light. They think I'm hypersensitive if not maniacal but it's all the same to me, it simplifies matters. The sidewalk opposite. I stopped in front of the neighbour's gate, that's incontestable. I thought again about a possible conversation and about Fonfon. I must have glanced through it but to see whether I could see Fonfon. He wasn't there. I looked to see whether there was a cat. No cat. A garden gnome. No garden gnome. A Grecian vase. No Grecian vase. But the garbage can was there all right. What if he'd thrown my ball into it? I had to speak to him. I certainly stayed quite a while in front of his gate. I could see the chair he sits on no doubt to read his newspaper. And against the wall, a rose called Star of Holland. Perhaps I also thought that we ought to plant one in our garden. It would climb up to the first floor, it would cheer things up. And a rose called Madame Butterfly. But we'd always be forgetting to water them, I mean Fonfon would, one more opportunity for a clout, I had to forget about it. An in any case, roses are quite expensive. We must remember the washing machine. That machine is really coming out of my nose. Gaston never talks about anything else these days. It's going to cause dreadful trouble with the laundress and with Marie too, she won't want to get landed with that work on top of everything else. Hasn't it already caused enough trouble? I rather think Gaston told me something of the sort. Unless I'm already imagining it, that's not difficult. And I came home.

Much longer than I said just now. I was wrong. It couldn't have been before ten o'clock. Marie had been out a good twenty minutes at least. Why was I sure I'd seen her? I won't explain that, it would be pointless. But I hadn't seen her, it was impossible. Hadn't seen her go out, I mean. She may quite well have told me from the window, seeing me go into the cellar, there are only three bottles left, tell Monsieur Gaston, please. Not while I was drinking my tea. At that moment. That's probable, that must be it. At all events I didn't see her go out. Therefore it's more or less certain that I didn't go into the kitchen. Nor go back into the refectory. Why would I have gone back there? Did Reber want to say something to me? No. Around ten o'clock these days she goes down into the garden, she doesn't go back into the refectory. Well, that was it, she went down into the garden and demanded her chair. She'll have called Fonfon, no answer, and I'll have said don't upset yourself, I'll take it out for you. But she did it herself. I can still see her. She had her knitting in one hand and with the other she was dragging the chair. I lent her one of my own hands. And when she'd got settled I quickly asked her or re-asked her whether she hadn't seen my paper. I was more specific, I said little ball. She shrugged her shoulders in the way that I've described and that I dislike. So that she shouldn't always treat me as an inferior I added that that ball, that paper, was of considerable importance, an entire paragraph of my memoir depended on it.

All my wits. It would be better if I were to lose them once and for all and say no more about them. There's no danger of that. I shall always keep enough of them to hope to lose them.

Wine, canary, ball, what else? There was something else. The wine is the most important, mustn't forget to tell Gaston.

I must have continued my round of the garden in spite of Reber. When I'd reached the craproom window I started on the middle third going from the house to the Rivoire wall. Near the trunk of the chestnut tree I raised my head but more to make sure that Fonfon wasn't in it. My ball couldn't have got stuck. Or did I think it might have been trapped in an intersection of two branches? I didn't insist because of Reber. I carried on up to the aucubas. Empty-handed. But I'd known for a long time that I'd end up empty-handed. Did Reber feel sorry for me? She must have said something to me at that moment, to give me something else to think about. She must have talked about her niece. She'd go in September or she wouldn't go. She would go this year. She hoped Madame Apostolos could go and stay with hers, that would give her something else to think about. And about the washing machine, she didn't altogether agree with Gaston, wouldn't a fridge be better. Look at the butter this morning, and the ratatouille doesn't even keep from one day to the next, not to speak of the potatoes. I said that the fridge would definitely only be any use for two months, July and August, but the machine all year round. She asked me insidiously how we'd managed to save such a sum. She probably thinks we're skimping on the everyday rations. I disabused her by telling her that we were buying it on the installment plan. This practically made her choke. She isn't used to that kind of purchase, they didn't go in for that sort of thing in the past, she supposes it's all right for the youth of today who have no conscience, no nothing, who borrow, who steal, and all the rest. How could *we* descend to that kind of thing. She told me once again about a hold-up in Agapa the other day perpetrated by some young people, she tars everyone with the same brush. Buying on the installment plan, she said, receiving credit... I wanted to make a play on words and tell her that people must give credit where credit is due. It was just as well I didn't. And I left her to her knitting. I went up to my room again.

There I reflected on what I had just done and whether I'd done it properly. I'd gone the rounds of the garden, right, but hadn't I done it knowing I wasn't going to find anything, just to have a clear conscience? A clear conscience! To think that we've been forced from childhood to put on that act. Yes, I'd gone the rounds knowing that I wasn't going to find anything. It's a very special mood and it's the only one that can work the miracle. You need to forget you're searching and yet go on searching. I'm not playing with words, I don't feel like it. A very special mood. I wasn't in it. I shall never manage to be in it. Should I even so have tried, that's to say gone down having forgotten why, and gone the rounds of the garden and looked elsewhere than on the ground, relaxed, thinking rather about the others, about my duties towards them, about the garden, the staircase, and the corridor that they see every day, trying to put myself in their shoes and feel sorry for them? That sort of thing. At first I went back to the window and watched Reber under the chestnut tree. Every so often she stopped and counted her stitches. She pushes her spectacles down to the tip of her nose, counts one purl one plain, and pushes them back again. She doesn't necessarily look at her work while she's knitting, after all this time she's used to it. She knits for the poor. She's certainly thinking about her life, about her nieces, about first communions, her school friends, storks. She pushes her spectacles down and counts. She pushes them back up. All those years, it's pretty short and it's pretty long. She hasn't had very much but you have to earn your place in heaven just the same. Knitting for the poor. She'll die at her knitting, thinking she hasn't knitted enough. God knows what she imagines paradise is like. A kind of sewing bee where everyone smiles, where you drink tea with sugar, where you sing compline, where you talk about days gone by? Why do I say that? It's probably all wrong but it reassures me. I wouldn't want her to imagine paradise in any other way. These failed lives spent in knitting for the poor, don't they make you want to vomit? I feel like vomiting, and that's why. I saw Reber, then. I was telling myself that I was already beginning to forget my whatsit, mustn't say the word paper, that I was maybe on the right track though I knew I wasn't but even so, even so there was a kind of let up. I shut my eyes to avoid the temptation of searching my room again, I only opened them again when I got to the stairs so as not to break my neck. I went down the stairs very slowly, putting myself in the place of Apostolos when she went up them. It must be pretty hard going. And those tacky bannisters that Marie forgets to wipe. It's Fonfon with his sticky hands, he's always pulling a bit of chewing gum or candy out of his mouth. Tell Marie about the bannisters. Wine, canary, ball, bannisters. I've never seen Apostolos doing anything other than limp. When she says it's worse you don't notice any difference. How to get her to understand that she's ridiculous with her violet hair and her red lips or vice versa? That then people might be more inclined to be sorry for her, to show her some affection? Doesn't she want affection? At all events, impossible to drop the slightest hint, even for her own good. Even Gaston with all his diplomacy couldn't. How he irritates me with his circumlocutions, when he's talking to the maids, for example! You have to be pretty subtle to know what he really means. Anyone outside the household would never understand. To say this glass is dirty, for instance, he'll say glasses are the first thing people look at on any self-respecting table, they notice the slightest smudge, fortunately that never happens in our house. That kind of remark. Marie does sometimes understand but she must have a bit of a private giggle.

When I'd got downstairs I decided to go straight over to Mademoiselle Reber. But so that she didn't think it strange, seeing that I don't like her any more than the rest of them do, I had to find a pretext. What did I find. The washing machine? No. The holidays? No. Fonfon. It's coming back to me, I found Fonfon. I'd tell her that she mustn't clout him. It would have been more charitable to talk to her about something that affected her personally but even so I can't always ask the impossible of myself. I told her, I wanted to talk to you about slapping, don't slap him, I'll take care of that, he'll end up being afraid of you and that would upset me. She looked at me over her glasses and said afraid? If only I *could* make him afraid of me but he doesn't care, he'll get his clout all right. I told her that she knew very well that it didn't do any good since he did it again. She said that the more you hit a nail the more it goes in, one of those phrases that infuriates me. Mustn't get worked up. I didn't exactly mean afraid, I told her, it's that I wouldn't like, how can I put it, I wouldn't like him to feel any less... well, any less affection for you because you slap him. She looked at me once again. Affection! Good heavens! Are you pulling my leg? That idiot! And besides, I would never try to gain his affection through an act of cowardice. He has to

mend his ways. That's the least I can do for him. His affection! You have
strange principles! Obviously I knew that that was what she'd reply.
Quick, find a ploy to make the conversation last. I said by the way do
you know whether Marie noticed that there wasn't any more cheese?
Whereupon, well, she looked me right in the face. Are you out of your
mind? You've just told her. I said oh so I have how stupid I am, and went
over to the gate. It was both a flop and not a flop, a bit of both, really.
But what exactly was I trying to do? To extract a smile from her? At all
events, it *was* I who had told Marie about the cheese. I ought to have
pointed out to Reber that I had insisted on her buying some blue. Maybe
that would have made her smile? But I'm going to get myself get
bogged down in this business of her smile and I don't think that's what I
was wanting. I let it go. Crushed. To put a good face on it and so that she
wouldn't ask me what I was doing by the gate, I went out into the street,
walked a couple of steps until I was hidden behind the wall, and looked
into the garden opposite. If Fonfon doesn't go there, if there isn't a cat,
maybe I could send Fonfon to say something to the neighbour but
what? What's been happening recently that might interest him? I couldn't
think. The refuse collection? A problem common to everyone concerned? His garbage can, that was it. I'd send Fonfon to ask him where
he'd got that magnificent garbage can. Fonfon would forget why I'd
sent him, he'd get in a muddle and come back and tell me the first thing
that came into his head or he wouldn't come back at all and that would
be a good excuse to go and apologize to the neighbour. I do apologize, it
was silly of me to send the lad, you can't have understood a thing but
ever since I noticed your magnificent garbage can I've been wanting to
ask you where you got it. May one know? That at least can't antagonize
him. He'll answer. I could hear myself elaborating on the subject of
garbage cans, on people's lack of taste, *he* at least had taste, it's in the
little things that it reveals itself, it's like your weathercock, it's so
original, where did you get it? He went on answering, he was all smiles,
the conversation lasted, it branched off on to his nieces. Well, there I was
unbeatable. I could tell him about all our guests' nieces, about all the
embroidered table mats, the words said all topsy-turvy, the adorable
little mistakes, mixing all the nieces up of course but what did that
matter? The neighbour began to open up, he asked me how come we'd
taken so long to make each other's acquaintance, he offered me a drink,
we sat down in his garden, I talked to him about botany and as it so
happened he was interested. It's rare for a damn fool bachelor in the

country or almost not to be interested in it. But in actual fact is he a
bachelor? Since he'd been telling me about his nieces, he must be. Yes,
he'd just told me that he'd been engaged in nineteen-fourteen but that
his fiancée had ditched him for an Englishman, he'd never got over it,
he'd remained a bachelor. Sensitive, what's more. The complete and
utter damn fool. But I'd overcome my repugnance, I hung around, I
talked and talked, I was forgetting it was lunch time, I asked him
whether he had seen my cheese, Marie, I mean, our maid you know, did
she, no, how stupid I am, you can't possibly know, but perhaps you've
seen my... Careful. Mustn't say the word paper. I've got off to a bad
start. He already takes me for a nutcase. I quickly tried to make up for it
and came out with the word importune, I'd thought of it when I came
down the first time. But it was too late, I was doing the opposite of what
was required, I was marking out the distances after the event, it was
wrecked, he was clamming up, I could see how embarrassed he looked
and as I stood up I once again put my foot in it by saying I hope he didn't
importune you.

Approximately that. I heard Reber calling what on earth are you
doing. I wasn't properly hidden, she could see me. I went back through
the gate and said, nothing, I was thinking about the scarecrow, what
sort of distance would it be effective over, do you think? She answered
why, do you want to plant some lettuces?

I've just said that sayings like one nail drives out another exasperate
me but that's when *she* says them. When it's me, I like them

No of course I don't want to plant any lettuces but I was telling
myself that it can't be effective as far as this garden because there's that
nest. It would suit me very well if it was effective over here, it would get
rid of the birds for us and our poor Fonfon would no longer be tempted
to climb the tree. She said it would be a sin to drive the birds away, the
Good Lord's creatures, when we didn't even have a fruit tree, and even if
we did have one she wouldn't approve, the neighbour, well, that was his
business, and in any case they eat all the vermin, so you see, we get the
worst of it in any case, nature must be allowed to take its course. She's
always saying it would be a sin and this infuriates me. But I didn't react,
this time I didn't react. I thought again about her paradise where they
count your sins at the ticket office and I smiled. She asked me why I was
smiling, I said I don't know, no reason, or rather, I was thinking about
the neighbour's vermin, he'll be had all right. I'd have done better to ask
her what she knew about the neighbour but I didn't think of it, he

doesn't interest me. Must repeat that he doesn't interest me. Or else it's my business, strictly personal. No gossip. She probably had it on the tip of her tongue to say something bitchy about the neighbour but she kept her trap shut. She knows I don't like that sort of thing. I've given a false impression of myself. They think I'm virtuous whereas I never stop calling everyone a damn fool. They can't see any difference between virtue and lack of interest even though it's fundamental. They're even the exact opposite of each other. In other words, virtue is saying bitchy things about your neighbours? Maybe, maybe. I'm weighing my words. In short, I no longer knew what to do to forget I was looking for my ball. I went over to the craproom window and said to Reber not lettuces, of course not, we haven't enough room but shouldn't we plant *something* as we did at the beginning, some touch-me-nots for instance, do you remember, wouldn't they make a cheerful sight? She said ah you see you *are* thinking of growing something, but in the first place the touch-me-nots weren't there they were under the refectory, personally I'd like nothing better than to plant some more but you don't seem to remember that you said they were hideous, that upset me a great deal at the time, back home in Alsace we're used to flowers, we love them, they're the Good Lord's creatures. She was off again. I said you should have told us, why didn't you tell us? We would have sown some more if it would have given you pleasure. There I'd gone too far. She was wondering what had got into me, she looked at me over her glasses and counted her stitches. I tried to make amends. You and the others, we've no reason not to give you that pleasure, you don't have a lot as it is. I was getting myself in even deeper. She must have told herself that I was having one of my turns, she didn't say any more. She knows me, she's well aware that it doesn't last. But if she wants to earn her place in heaven, the idiot, she'd do better to try to make my turns last instead of reimmersing herself in her knitting.

I dropped it. I went into the cellar telling myself that I hadn't properly checked whether there really were only three bottles left, this surprised me. Marie might not have seen properly, you can't see a thing in the cellar. I switched on the light. I thought we really might treat ourselves to a stronger bulb. Mention it to Gaston. I went over to the far end and counted the bottles again. There were only three, it was quite true. Tell Gaston wine. Wine, canary, bulb, and what else? Next I looked at the coal. Did we need to order some more? And the potatoes. Would there be enough when the hordes returned? I wasn't really

wondering, I was just dillydallying. I didn't want to resurface, to see
Reber again, to have her ask me again what I was doing. But if I stayed
too long in the cellar she would also ask me. I'm fed up. I can't go on
living like this. Something has to be changed. Well, I'll talk to her about
the potatoes, I'll answer that I was counting them, that's it. That's what I
said to myself. And if she shrugged her shoulders I'd tell her that her
Alsace and her first communions, she could stuff them you know
where. Why not? We should see. That would change something. What
would she do? Would she shout for help? Would she shit her pants?
What would she do? I can still see myself, I was sitting on the heap of
coal, when I'm usually so careful about my trousers, they'd be black all
over. I was really in a state. And I couldn't resurface. If she shat her pants
no one would see. Unless she shouted for help at the same time? Gaston
would show up pronto. Where *was* Gaston all this time? In the refectory,
at the catafalque, going through the bills and double-checking them.
The catafalque is a writing desk in black-varnished pine, that's what we
call it. Gaston spends his whole life going through bills and double-
checking them. At this moment he must be doing some sums in
connection with the washing machine, we're going to have to pay the
first installment. Actually, maybe that's what I was talking to him about
this morning? Let me think. I go into the refectory. Ghastly light, smell
of burned fat, flies. I say to myself, another day, filthy July, when will it
end. And the washing machine again, he's going to talk to me about the
machine again. All this in a quarter of a second. I automatically look
around at the catafalque, he's there. That's it. He was there. I sat down in
my place. We haven't said good morning to each other for a long time.
Not that we don't like each other or that we've quarrelled, no. But
there's no point. We keep that for the guests. We've become economical
even with words and I don't regret it. One of the only things I don't
regret. Do I regret so many as all that? Sincerely. I don't think so, all in
all. Nothing else could have happened to me. Whatever I've done I've
done for the best. Especially the damn silly things. I couldn't have done
things any differently, I couldn't see how to do things any differently.
Otherwise I would have. Therefore I don't regret anything. I seem as if
I'm fiddle-faddling at this moment but not in the least. I'm packing my
bag. I don't regret anything, that would be absurd. I have a horror of the
absurd. Gaston was at the catafalque and I said something to him but
what? Not right away. Waiting for my tea to cool. What did I say that I
said to Reber? What I said to Gaston must have been more or less

important. The wine? No, that was the first time I came down and I hadn't seen Marie yet. But if I hadn't seen her at all, then she hadn't said anything about the wine to me? I must have passed her in the corridor after my tea. Unless she came in after I'd spoken to Gaston? No, it would have been him she told about the wine. Did she say it to me or not?

All my wits. Mustn't get worked up. Keep calm. Wine, canary, bulb. I pour out my tea. I wait for it to cool. Gaston is going through his bills. I tell myself that he's going to talk to me about the machine. To avoid that, I say something to him to start him off on another tack. No matter what. Has Fonfon taken out Reber's chair? He doesn't answer. I look out of the window. It isn't out. I say he's going to get himself slapped again, couldn't you tell Reber not to overdo it. He doesn't answer. You might at least answer me. What? I repeated my sentence. He said look, that's not my department, deal with it yourself, I have enough to do as it is. I'd goofed, he was going to talk about the machine. But if I didn't say anything he'd be off again. So I had to think of something else. Let's not forget that this is my first time down, I've only just got out of bed. I'm still in a haze. Nothing I've said up to now has happened yet, neither the paper, nor the insults, nor the neighbour, nor anything. I start to drink my tea. That was it. I said maybe we ought to try Ceylon tea, the Magasins-Prix have some that's quite cheap. He again said what. I was disturbing him, he wanted to be left alone, he wasn't going to mention the machine. Phew. I drank my tea. Marie came in just as I was putting my cup down. She put the dishes away in the sideboard. She didn't say anything about the wine at that moment. Unless she told me in an undertone so as not to disturb Gaston? She's very considerate towards him. I don't think so. I'd still be hearing her whispering in my ear or I should still be smelling her bad breath. They all have bad breath in this dump. Including me. They say it comes from the stomach but personally I say it comes from the heart. I should remember if she'd spoken to me in a low voice because I have a horror of that. She didn't mention the wine to me at that moment. Afterwards. When I went down into the garden again. Right. I put my cup down and didn't wait for any more, I went out.

All that just to know where Gaston was. I've got up to Reber shitting her pants. Did I really imagine the scene while I was in the cellar? It's possible but then it must have been very quick, I didn't linger. What I was actually doing was trying to find a way to get out of the cellar without Reber speaking to me. Or did I really want to stay there? No, I don't think so. Maybe I said to myself if only we could stay here like this sitting on a heap of coal and be left in peace. This crossed my mind but it didn't last. I must have told myself let's go out and if she asks me what I was doing I'll say I was wondering whether Fonfon had hidden the nest in the cellar. He collects nests even though he knows we forbid it. He's put them somewhere in the shed, that I know, but he may have told himself that I'd discovered where they were, and the last nest, the one we've been talking about these last few days, a chaffinch's nest or something of the sort, might he have hidden it in the cellar? Why not. Say that to Reber. And I went out. She wasn't on her chair. Wasted effort. She must have gone to pee or to get some different needles from her room. I mustn't think about my ball any more but even so I had to stay in the garden just in case... I went over to the refectory window and looked to see whether Gaston was still there. He wasn't. I went over to the craproom side and looked in. He was there, looking for a book in the shelves. I asked him what it was and I added while I think of it there are only three bottles left in the cellar, you'd better order some more. He said remind me later, I'm busy.

I've got up to the third time I came down counting the one for my tea, or is it the fourth. I want to find my ball without looking for it, by getting interested in something else, by being pleasant if possible. I again asked Gaston what book, he replied a thriller for Apostolos. I couldn't insist further or he'd have thought me suspect. Suspect isn't the word. He'd have said to himself he's having one of his turns, but coming from him that thought didn't bother me, it couldn't humiliate me. Yet I preferred him not to think it so that I could try and remain spontaneous, say something nice to him that wouldn't make him smell out anything like a turn, using another tone of voice, as you might say, another register. Still on account of my ball, of course. I had to provoke a miracle, hence not flounder about in the familiar. I had a lot of trouble finding something, that I do remember. This sort of situation is rather sad. Trying to be pleasant without making people smell a rat. It's probably impossible since you're forcing yourself but I'm simply describing what happens to me, without avoiding the issue. I couldn't completely forget, either, to look at the gravel, at the same time forgetting I was looking at it. Then Gaston went out of the craproom. I had no one left to prove my spontaneous niceness to. Reber would be coming down again but I'd already tried it with her and if I tried it again it would come to a bad end. Better leave it at that, that's what I thought. The thriller gave me an idea. I'd go and sit on the steps with a book, I'd be pretending to read it to stop her annoying me and every so often I'd look at the gravel, thinking of something else. That might work. I went into the craproom. I couldn't find a thriller, I took out Therese Neumann, * the first book that came to hand, and went and sat down on the steps again, the bottom one. If she asked me why I didn't get a chair I'd answer that I feel like sitting here, like at the beginning, you remember, before the factory. Maybe I could even be pleasant, talking about that, about the past, maybe she wouldn't jib? Oh yes she would, though, the touch-me-nots. I gave up that idea and pretended to be reading, all the while preparing my spontaneous response.

Are we going around in circles? We're going around, perhaps, but not in circles. I notice that in spite of everything I've managed to get something out of this morning. Maybe I'll get on the track of my paper this way, I'm still hoping. It's always when I'm mulling over what I've done that ideas occur to me about what I ought to have done. No question of regrets, in this case. A little oversight this morning and I can put it right tomorrow. I'm full of hope.

Reber came down again. She passed me without opening her mouth, sat down on her chair again and started knitting again. Without even raising her eyes. I went on pretending to read, and one thing leading to another I wasn't looking at the gravel. This seemed idiotic to me, there was nothing more to be seen within a radius of three meters at the outside, I might just as well go back up to my room. I couldn't count on the miracle, I had to find something else. A different technique. A different frame of mind. Up till now, when I looked for something it had always been feverishly. That was why I fatigued myself and irritated everyone. I had to change myself, I had to bring about a great revolution. Be someone else. And end up never losing anything whatsoever, never forgetting anything. I could see myself all white, all hoary, wearing an oriental loincloth. I didn't have a house any more, I lived in the market-place and other people, the people who lost things, came and consulted me about how to find them. It was July, it was abominably hot, there were flies everywhere. Mademoiselle Reber was shaking me. Wake up, you'll get sunstroke, go up to your room until lunchtime. I wonder now whether that dream wasn't right. Is it normal to spend your whole time looking for something? No matter what different methods I use, they'll always be a plaster cast fitted on to a wooden leg.

It's the essential that needs to be changed. To change something, we're always coming back to that. I shouldn't have noted down that little dream, it's idiotic. Said like that, it's idiotic. I shouldn't have implied that I fell asleep. I let myself drift into a kind of fatigue which made me talk about fatigue. This mustn't happen again.

Maybe say something about the craproom. The allegory, for example. It's a bronze, representing a naked woman letting her scarf trail behind her. Half tangled-up in the scarf are a couple of dwarfs or a couple of children who are teasing a wild boar. The wild boar is apparently snoozing. His front paws are resting on the feet of a young man who's leaning over to the left as if he wanted to avoid touching the lady. It's totally hideous, but Gaston wants to keep it. I can understand him wanting to keep useful things however horrible, I'd be the first to tell him to keep them if he wanted to get rid of them, but that thing. Obviously, it came down to him from his grandmothers, it's sacred. If at least we could lose it. Often in the winter, then, or even in the spring or autumn, to pass the time in the evenings we ask each other what it means. Opinions vary. I don't think I'll enumerate them now. Given my slight state of fatigue I re-risk falling asleep and I have to get ahead. Though you probably won't avoid them later on. Also in the craproom is a piano on which Madame Erard massacres the Turkish March and drowns the Trout. She has a kind of flabby touch, you can barely recognize the pieces. She plays on someone's birthday for instance or at Christmas or on the Fourteenth of July. To me, music makes sad evenings even sadder. You can think of nothing but the troubles and bereavements you've had all your life. Opposite the piano is a hulking great sofa where Elvira has her confinements. Elvira is the cat. Confinements isn't the right word. I probably won't get another chance to talk about Elvira because she's never there except to have her kittens. We cover the hulk with lots of papers and rags. Why is she never there? I've no idea. At all events, I never see her. Does she stay in the kitchen? In that case I would see her from time to time. Or in the maids' room? Where does she lurk all the time? Ask Gaston. Above the hulk there's a patch of mould on the wall and a bit above the patch the portrait of the Empress Eugénie. Do I have to tell about the other things? To disgust people with objects, yes. In one corner, behind the door leading into the corridor, there's a tradescantia in a flowerpot holder. The popular name for tradescantia is the misery plant because it grows everywhere. The pot holder is in the shape of a pumpkin, it reposes on a tripod consisting of three storks back to back. One has a mended beak, another has lost one of its feet but the remaining ones are enough for it to balance on. Gaston has a whole lot more things that came down to him from his grandmothers but fortunately, fortunately we didn't have room for them in the house. We distributed some of them here and there in the bedrooms and the rest are on top of the cupboard in the refectory. Things like a bronze Hermes, a Houdon★ plaster cast, an imitation Carpeaux★ on a carriage clock, all the phony divinities of the last century. They've been put with the objects which are no longer any use except when there's a storm, kerosene lamps, night-lights, spirit burners. Which is logical. I mean that for me it's logical. What else is there in the craproom? A mirror-wardrobe that's too big for the bedrooms, we keep the spare bed linen in it. A cupboard where the ladies keep their needlwork and bits of material. Another in which Monsieur Perrin keeps his newspaper cuttings about the Dreyfus affair, the Suez affair, the Stavisky affair, please excuse the chronology. It's the cupboard where we keep the illustrated magazines, *Illustration, Petite Illustration, Jardin des Modes,* the Saint-Etienne firearms catalogue. And Dutch bulb catalogues. And wrapping paper, shoe boxes, tool boxes. I'm falling asleep. Courage. I can't think about the wardrobe without seeing Madame Apostolos trying on a dress in front of it. Last year she'd decided to make herself a summer dress for her visit to her niece. Madame Erard was helping her sew it and try it on. She opened the wardrobe door and made it into a screen, telling us turn your backs, gentlemen. Madame Apostolos limped behind it to put the dress on. As if we had any wish to see her in her slip or God knows what. The gentlemen turned their backs without even looking up, they were reading or playing cards. Then Apostolos came out of her hiding place and appeared in the dress which had big purple flowers on an emerald background. She's mad on purple. She stood in front of the mirror, Madame Erard went down on her knees in front of her with the pins in her mouth and made her turn around while she adjusted the length of the dress. And the hippopotamus turned around and thought she looked beautiful. Doesn't that make you want to vomit, too? To weep while you're vomiting? I have nothing to relate but things like these. She won't have a chance to wear her dress again this year, poor woman, because she isn't going to her niece's. It'll be for next year. I can't remember what she told me, why she wasn't going. I rather think her nephew-in-law is setting her niece against or could it be her sister, the mother of her niece, who can't stand her? There were already scenes last year, Apostolos wept when she described them. Or was it Reber?

I've finished with the craproom. Just put on record that by the misery plant there's a cupboard in which Gaston keeps his photo albums. He always used to be taking photos, less these days. We also spend some evenings looking through the albums.

A word too about Madame Erard, since she's already butted in on the scene. She and her husband were our third or fourth guests. Or fifth? Their room is on the right of the stairs when you get to the first floor. To the right, opposite. It's simple, their room is the first on the garden side, above the refectory. He is a sales representative, in his fifties. She's in her thirties, she was his secretary in a stockings firm that went bust. They regularized their situation. As he doesn't earn enough to keep them both she makes rag dolls and sells them to the blind who resell them as their own work. She never stops talking about how many dolls she still has to make before noon or before midnight. What you might call on their uppers. When they first came there was always one of them whose liver was playing up and who didn't come down to dinner. This was so that we would deduct the price of a meal. When Gaston realized he insisted that both of them should eat, we'd give them credit. This is the only case at the guest house. From time to time a little credit here or there but not permanently. I've already said this.

Repeat, I'm looking for that paper.

And just as Reber was sending me back up to my room, Marie came back from her shopping. She said what heat, there's a drought, vegetables have gone up again. As it is we can't eat steak every day, if we have to go without vegetables as well, what's left. Pasta and rice? Even so, she'd bought some eggplants and zucchini seeing that there aren't very many of us but they were almost a luxury. She said they were almost a luxury. What else did she say? That she'd met a lady who'd told her that if we were ever stuck for a maid she could provide us with one. Marie had jotted down the phone number on a bit of paper, she looked for it in her handbag but couldn't find it. That's stupid she said, it could always come in handy, I put it in here but I can't find it. She searched all through her handbag, then she searched her shopping bag. The paper was there, underneath an eggplant. Ah, here it is. I said you see how you can mislay a bit of paper or put it down somewhere or other and forget where. She said it wasn't somewhere or other seeing that it's here, are you saying that because you haven't found yours? Do you still believe I

threw it away? Have you asked Mademoiselle Reber? I rather think
Reber winked at her, I wouldn't swear to it but I rather think so. This
happens more and more frequently with them. I said who is that
woman? Marie said here's her number and she handed me the paper.
No, the one who spoke to you. It was a neighbour of the plumber. She
added oh drat, I forgot the plumber again. We've had a leak in the
kitchen for a few days, Gaston had told Marie not to forget the plumber.
He comes back every year for that leak. Where did I put that telephone
number? It might come in useful if we were ever stuck. Why did she say
that? Why did she take that number? Does she want to go on holiday
too? I'll never dare ask her. Tell Gaston Marie. She asked me if I'd told
Gaston about the wine. Not yet, he's busy at the moment, I'll remind
him later. She went to the kitchen. What time could it have been? Half
past ten, something like that, that's more or less when she comes back
from her shopping. Reber went into the kitchen with her to help her
peel the eggplants. I sat down for a moment on the green chair, having
first wiped it with a leaf. I was thinking about Marie's holiday, what's
she cooking up. Unless her niece was ill? She often gets ill and Marie
goes and gives her a hand with the children. Already last year. And the
year before. Has Marie had a letter? No, she'd have told us. Last year,
when she had to go during the summer instead of in September, I wasn't
at all pleased. Nor was Gaston. It was Reber who did everything, she
ordered us about. Had she come to some sort of arrangement with
Marie? To get her to go away before September so she could order us
about? No. Marie wouldn't come to any sort of arrangement with her
even if it suited her. Fortunately, they detest each other. But why that
number? Reber immediately said, I remember, yes indeed that might be
useful if we ever get stuck. What does that mean? Especially as if we ever
did get stuck she would be giving the orders, like last year? Absolutely
essential to talk to Gaston about it. Wine, canary, bulb, getting stuck. I
can forget about the canary, that isn't urgent. What did I do while they
were peeling the eggplants? Did I stay on my chair? I think so, yes. What
about Therese Neumann? I still had it in my hand. I re-thought that I
might take advantage of re-thinking about something else so as to look
on the ground. While Reber wasn't observing me, that was easier. I
re-thought about the neighbour opposite, that's what's worrying me at
the moment. Perhaps a sign. I do sometimes get worried by things that
are going to happen. I must search over on that side. There's no point in
sending Fonfon as a scout. Go myself. Ask him where he got his

garbage can. What if he isn't in his garden? I can't ring his bell for that, can I? Why not? Between neighbours and during the holiday period that can't annoy him. Say importune. He said importune me, what do you mean? And I didn't know whether he didn't understand the word or whether he meant you must be joking. That's one more thing to consider, not to disconcert him right from the start. Not have to translate for him as well, that would be grotesque, and there he might take umbrage. Say take umbrage too. In the course of the conversation. I made amends by saying I'm not disturbing you am I, I hope I'm not disturbing you, he again said what do you mean. Therefore he had understood and he was using the expression what do you mean to mean you must be joking. Funny idea. If every time I don't understand what someone's saying to me I thought he was joking that would make my life much simpler. I don't joke enough. That's the sort of thing that has to be changed. Take everything as a laugh. Would that really simplify things? Wouldn't I be asking myself what exactly they are joking about or whether they're going to understand my joke? In general that's what people understand the least. That's not the solution. I'd given up the scarecrow and the weathercock and even the garbage can. I'd crossed the road, I'd glanced into his garden, he was there, we found ourselves face to face, and taken unawares I'd said good morning. It was so simple. But you also have to be taken unawares. Yes, it's coming back to me now. After that, fine day isn't it? Almost too fine, he had to spend his whole time watering the garden. His eggplants weren't doing too well, they're at the far end, over there, see, and I get tired carrying all those watering cans. I jumped at the opening saying yes I know, our maid has just told us that they're prohibitive, a real luxury, vegetables are all going up. The conversation had got off to a good start, it continued. He found me so pleasant that he was amazed we hadn't made one another's acquaintance before and he offered me a drink. He said will you help me bring the little table out of the shed. He too has a shed at the back of his house, I helped him bring the little table out and he went into the kitchen to fetch his Pernod. He came back with it and then I goofed. I was so pleased to drink a Pernod that I said I don't often drink it. I immediately thought he'll take us for down-and-outs. To make up for it I nearly said because it doesn't agree with me. That would have been pleasant! Fortunately the name Gaston came to my lips. It didn't agree with him and we'd got out of the habit of buying any. But in the old days, my goodness me! What couldn't I put away during those Pernod sessons! He liked my spontaneity, he felt very much at his ease, very cordial. So much so that I wondered whether I oughtn't to offer to carry his watering cans for him. These things to do or not to do, should I or shouldn't I, that's what ruins my existence. From that moment on I felt rather less pleased. It seemed to me that the Pernod wasn't really so very extraordinary. Did he notice my slight embarrassment? I was once again in a spot, telling myself that even so it really was exasperating, when just for once I could have relaxed and those watering cans had to spoil all my pleasure. It wasn't the watering cans, it was my nature that needed to be changed but at the time, maybe because of the Pernod, I thought it was the watering cans. Finally I was so embarrassed that I told myself I must stand up, I must go, I can't mention my paper to him now. Perhaps that was precisely what I should have done, to change the atmosphere. I'd have had to tell him about my botany as he might well have been interested in it, I'd thought before that he was interested in it, him being a damn fool bachelor. It was ruined. When all of a sudden his cat came out of the kitchen. I said puss puss, to attract it. Spontaneous again. I was thanking heaven as I stroked it, maybe things would start up again. And they did, quite simply, quite easily, quite stupidly. I didn't need to cudgel my brains. He said do you like cats? I spoke about Elvira that I never see. He told me that our... our... he didn't how to put it, our young lad was very fond of his cat, he came and played with it. So as not to elaborate on our poor Fonfon I simply said oh yes, and once again heaven had thrown me a line and I said spontaneously, there are an awful lot of cats in our neighbourhood. He said do you often go for walks. I said I went herborizing in the wood. There we were, I could talk about my botany! I was so pleased to have forgotten my malaise that I forgot to mention the paper to him. I talked and talked, I let myself go, I wasn't being very careful any more, or let's say I was being less careful. I talked about our life, about my meeting with Gaston, without going into detail about his diarrhea, about our buying the dump, about the repairs, the faucets, the lino. He well remembered it, of course he did, he even remembered that the truck had got stuck in the mud some ten meters at the most before our garden, Gaston and I had pushed it, we'd put some planks under the rear wheels, he'd have been glad to give us a hand but he'd been taking a foot bath, he could see us from his bathroom window, the first one facing the road. I had been pretty sure that was the bathroom. He too had troubles with the plumber, the outlet, pipes needing to be changed. He didn't have the same plumber as us. I recommended ours but they're all alike, the first thing they need to do is learn their trade. And the neighbour repeated I've been wanting to make your acquaintance for so long, I'd finally given up hope. Just imagine, I don't know whether I can say this to you, go ahead, just imagine, I thought you were stuck-up, you must excuse me. I said well I don't know, that's funny, did you really think that? The ideas we can get into our heads! And I went further. I said we're all in the same boat, telling myself that I was going too far but so what, when just for once I'm drinking Pernod? Maybe it was that. Because when he offered me another I didn't say no. I knew that I was going to go far too far in my confidences but I didn't say no. It was in the lap of the gods. Come what may. Next I spoke about the arrival of Mademoiselle Reber, our first customer. He remembered it very well, even that she'd left a suitcase behind at the station. I didn't react to that because all the women had left a suitcase behind at the station. He was also surprised that he hadn't got to know our guests either. Obviously it was abnormal, maybe not the men, who mostly go out to work, but the women, who are more inclined to talk and who have nothing to do. But he ended up telling me that it was his fault, he's very shy. What bothered him was that he was afraid our guests would think him stuck-up. He was telling me everything, you see. I said you, stuck up? Are you joking? I shall tell them that you're the best neighbour, the very best, and you'll see, they'll speak to you. But maybe he doesn't want them to any more? Have I gone too far? Even if I ask him he'll say can you doubt it, still want them to, but only to be polite. All that time he hadn't spoken to them, he'd learned to make the best of it and also he might have changed. You do change with age, and he was ten years older. He must be seventy. And also maybe he foresaw that the first person to take advantage of my invitation would be Marie and as it happened he didn't like her? The only one he didn't want to speak to? But I was less worried after my second Pernod, I went on talking about our life. The only thing I was being really careful about was not to say that we were broke. From time to time I glanced over at our façade and I thought it didn't look too bad, well, it was tolerable, no one would suspect that everything inside was so squalid. And when he spoke about our guests he called them those ladies and gentlemen, that was a good sign. Distances. At the third Pernod—the third or the second?—at the third I told him first Gaston's name, then everyone else's. The thin little lady who sits in the garden at this time of year is Mademoiselle Reber, then, she's Alsatian from top to bottom, and I emphasized the word bottom. The maid who does the shopping is Marie, then, her niece is married, her nephew-in-law can't stand her, she's divorced, she has a beard as you know, she's ugly as you know. Madame Sougneau is the cook, she's a widow, she has a daughter... a daughter she hardly ever sees, and nieces too, she's on holiday at the moment. He said he'd seen her getting into the bus. That bus is very convenient, right in front of the gate, we couldn't ask for anything better. Do you take advantage of it? He replied very little, I go out very little, it's more that it's useful for my visitors. He had visitors and I didn't know! What kind of visitors, your family? Yes, nieces. He had such an adorable little great-niece, can you imagine, at her age she already embroiders place mats, she uses adorable words, all topsy-turvy, for example to say embroider she says embwoider and for little she says likkle. At any rate she must know how to say caca. That's just me exaggerating. And the gentleman who's still on the youngish side, that was Monsieur Vérassou, he works at the hospital as a laboratory assistant. And the gentleman who's rather fattish, in his fifties, what am I saying, fifties, he must be sixty by now, it was ten years ago that he was in his fifties and his wife in her thirties, can Madame Erard already be forty? Of course she can, you only have to work it out. Well, this gentleman who is married, I didn't say they'd regularized their situation, married to a younger lady, is Monsieur Erard. He's a sales representative. His wife, Madame Erard that is, makes very pretty rag dolls that she sells. Nor did I say to the blind, we never know what we have coming to us. And the lady who's old, too, but tall, very gaunt, very pale, who looks like an Englishwoman on holiday, well that's Madame Cointet, and her husband, that's Monsieur Cointet, the thin little old man with a goatee beard, and the fat, red-faced man who goes fishing, that's Monsieur Perrin, oh yes, very jovial, very good-natured, you'd get on well with him, he's always cracking jokes, that boosts your morale. I didn't tell him that his jokes get on your nerves, they're always the same, it wasn't the moment. Maybe even, thinking back to Perrin's jokes after the fourth Pernod, third or fourth? third, I did think them funny and didn't have to stop myself telling him they got on your nerves? I did think them funny, quite so. This Pernod, what a godsend. I must persuade Gaston to buy some again. He'll pull a long face but so what. If only we could all take to it! No more evenings that make you want to vomit. Or rather, we would vomit, but we'd know what. Tell Gaston Pernod. Wine, bulb, Pernod.

He'd seen them all go away on holiday except the portly elderly lady with the flowered dress. Madame Apostolos, yes, no, she's still here, she isn't going away this year, she doesn't get on with her niece or her sister any more, she made herself a dress especially to go away with, she won't have a chance to wear it, the quarrel has just come to a head, a definite break by letter, a dress she'd made with Madame Erard's help, I'd got it all wrong, I was mixing up the years, I went even further, I all but said and what when that happens to us, to make ourselves dresses we shan't be able to wear, I was pissed, my glottis was beginning to vibrate, I couldn't stop talking, I spoke of my own nieces, the day when they would drop me completely, even now it isn't like it used to be, I shan't be able to take an interest in botany any longer, my sight won't be good enough, what shall I do, what shall I hold on to, to the tables and chairs like the blind, so now I was blind, I could see myself dragging my steps from the craproom to the catafalque, Gaston had been dead a long time, it was my job to check the bills, I couldn't see a thing, instead of helping me Marie read out all the wrong figures on purpose, she left me to do the best I could and jot down my sums on odd bits of paper that I couldn't see, I wrote on the blotting paper, I dragged myself to the bog thinking of poor dead Apostolos, I was stricken with remorse, we ought to have helped her, we used to let her go upstairs by herself, it's frightful how painful it is, I knew from experience, I groped my way over to the pan and pissed to one side, when it wasn't beforehand, on the stairs, Marie yelled you old pig you do it on purpose, she came and clouted me, my Fonfon, my poor Fonfon, what became of him, I let him be slapped all his life, where is he now? In a hospital? Has he got incurable slapitis? All swollen, all deformed, you can't see his eyes any more, his gentle, idiot's eyes, his mouth, his beautiful hair.

When I found myself back on my chair I was afraid one or the other would come back and ask me what I was doing. I quickly stood up and went out of the gate into the street. Hidden by the Rivoire wall. I looked up at the weathercock, I said to myself, getting myself into such a state. I heard Reber shouting but what are you doing. She could see me from the garden, I wasn't properly hidden. I answered, nothing, do you know where Fonfon is? And I went back. I was looking for Fonfon, what could be more natural? She shrugged her shoulders. She sat down again and said don't go away, the eggplants will soon be cooked, why didn't you go up and have a rest? What had got into the old madwoman? Was she worrying about my health, now? What had changed her mood? Peeling the eggplants? With Marie, that was it. They'd been chatting, they detested each other less than I thought, they were plotting something. She was being pleasant to prepare the trick of the substitute, she'd find it easier to persuade us not to get anyone in, to let her manage things as she did last year. Marie was going away. That was it, that was certainly it. Talk to Gaston about it right away, I'd forgotten again. Tomorrow at the earliest opportunity. I said I don't feel tired, anyone can fall asleep in the sun with this heat, what weather don't you think, there's been nothing like it for the last fifty years, they said so on the radio. And I sat down beside her on the green chair. After having avoided her so much for an hour, two hours, I don't know any longer, after having prepared phrases, excuses, evasions, I was sitting beside her! I can't explain it. Or perhaps the only possible explanation is the change in her tone. She wasn't aggressive when she asked me why I hadn't gone up to have a rest. This ought to have worried me, she was certainly plotting with Marie, no though, as calm as anything. And the miracle happened, not the one I was expecting, I was genuinely pleasant. All of a sudden no shadow of embarrassment, not even of suspicion. I asked her how her niece was, whether the storks had come back to the same place, if they'd written to her, if she really was going away at the beginning of September. She stopped knitting. Another miracle. She told me yes, she was going, she was very much looking forward to it, it would give her something else to think about. Her niece had just had a third daughter, she would be able to give her a hand, it couldn't have come at a better time. The oldest one had made her first communion in May, she had a photo, she'd show it to me after lunch. The second one was adorable, she embroidered little place mats, her niece had written to her that there were some waiting for her, a surprise. Those dear little girls, if I didn't have them I don't what I'd do. What could I hold on to? Oh, I know very well that in a few years' time it will all be different, they will grow away from me, they won't love me any more, just thinking about it frightens me. Because my niece is very sweet but you know how it is, her husband, my nephew-in-law that is, calls me an old madwoman when I'm not there, I know he does, I won't tell you how but I know it. He thinks that a month's holiday with them puts a strain on their budget, that I get the little girls into bad habits and this and that. It won't be very long before he sets my niece against me. Before my nieces stop loving me. And that's that. I told her that she mustn't look on the black side of everything, what the devil, her nephew might change, especially this year when he would see how much easier she made things for her niece, he'd be grateful to her. May God hear you, she said. But it isn't only that, it's my sister, she detests me. She lives very near them and just seeing me turn up will make her fly off the handle again. I said Mademoiselle. I don't know any more what I said. I must have said the same thing to Apostolos. At one moment we were talking about Madame Sougneau and she told me I ought to tell her to change her apron more often. For her part, she didn't dare. It had to be either me or Gaston. I said I'll make a note of it, I'll tell him when he comes back, it's a rather delicate matter but we'll manage. And one thing leading to another, the washing machine. I had it coming to me. I began to unmellow. It's going to get worse every day. When the others are back it's all we shall ever speak of. Unmellowed. I told myself we must react, we must change the subject. I brought up the niece with the place mat again but the moment had passed. I brought up the storks again, idem. She went back to the machine, to the expense, it didn't seem reasonable to her. A fridge, that I wouldn't say, look at the butter this morning, and the ratatouille doesn't keep a couple of days in this heat, to say nothing of the potatoes. I repeated that we'd only use the fridge for about two months, whereas the machine. As if I was interested. I felt it was more appropriate to stand up for Gaston. To steer her away from the subject I said I was thinking over what you said about the flower bed, if we planted it with nasturtiums we'd be able to have some cut flowers, what do you think? She replied that anything would be better than that frightful empty bed. Let her go and buy some seeds and plant them herself then, the cuntess. Fonfon picks pathetic bunches of flowers in the fields, they break my heart but the others couldn't care less. Even Reber with her nature. He picks buttercups in the spring, their stalks all different lengths, daisies that wither in a quarter of an hour and hideous little blue flowers whose name I don't yet know. I tried to find it in my plant guide but it keeps referring you to a figure according to the number of petals, the shape of the leaves and so on, and the net result is that I land up among the orchids every time, it can't be that. Yes, Fonfon's bunches of flowers. I had to insist on him being allowed to put them in a vase and on the table himself. The guests have had to resign themselves to it but they guffaw. And my Fonfon must realize it in spite of everything because I took him out herborizing with me once and he picked me some flowers. He ran ahead to a spot he knew and brought them back to me saying I've picked you some campanalas because you're the only one who loves me.

Some campanalas.

After that I said to Reber...

I'm tired. It'll pass. This exposé is killing me. I have to go quickly and I'm not used to it.

I told her that in the coming year we were going to have the rooms repainted. Gaston and I had talked about it. During the holidays. So the best thing for her would be to tell her niece that she'd spend July and August with her. For you, so that you aren't inconvenienced by the work, the smells. I was thinking for *us*, Gaston and I couldn't have her under our feet all the time. She said after what I've just been telling you about my nephew-in-law? I'm not even sure I shall be able to go back there next September. I told her again not to worry, everything would work out all right, she ought to think about letting her niece know. You understand, it's ten years since they were done, ten years, doesn't time fly. And to soften her, do you remember when you moved in? You'd left a suitcase behind at the station. That's true, she said. And your room was all blue, all freshly-painted, didn't you like it? It must be pretty faded by now. That's true, there are patches of mould that I've tried to remove with soapy water and the colour on the paper ran, and the wainscoting is dirty and so is the door, rather than light grey I'd prefer the doors, all the doors, to be painted beige. I said that that was a colour that soon turned yellow, it wasn't economical. What about your grey then, don't you think that's turned yellow?

Repeat, I'm a decent fellow, on a rather small scale.

What time could it have been, would it soon be midday, so we could eat the eggplants.

No, it still wasn't midday. I told myself it still wasn't midday, why did she tell me not to go away, that the eggplants would soon be ready? She could see I wasn't wearing my watch. But I might look at the alarm clock in the kitchen or go up to my room? She knows me. She knew that if I went up to my room I should forget that it was to see what time it was. And that I would prefer to go and see in my room. To stay there, and not budge until midday, until she called me. How did she know that I wouldn't ask *her* the time? I'm going to tell you how she knew. She knows how discreet I am. To ask her ah yes what's the time would be to doubt what she'd told me, that the eggplants would soon be ready, I wouldn't dare. Since she wanted to send me up to my room I wouldn't go. I stood up, I went over towards the front door steps to raise her hopes, and then I turned back and went to the shed. I darted a quick glance to see her mug. These little acts of revenge aren't pretty but they're all I have. They're all I have to settle my nerves. I have an idea that they calm me. Once I was in the shed I didn't know what to do there. I'd already inspected everything. Well then, I'd start again, to give Reber a pain in the ass. This was also a way of provoking the miracle. Of looking while at the same time telling myself I'm giving Reber a pain in the ass, that was a way of forgetting that I was looking.

I didn't come out right away. Once again I had what they call a presence. A sudden change of ideas. Looking at the toad-in-the-hole table. I thought back to the time when we used to play this game with Gaston and the others. It passed the time on Sundays and July evenings. How young we were! To be capable of amusing ourselves for hours at missing that toad. It's only very rarely that you manage to throw the disc into the toad's mouth. Didn't we invite other people too? I must try to remember, I feel it's important. Yes of course, there were other people. Neighbours? Or nieces? Did they invite their nieces? I have an impression of a crowd and of young people. Their nieces, of course it was, not their great-nieces at that period, their nieces ten years ago. I seem to see some young girls. Ugly ones, for the most part. With greasy hair and spots, who are all the time forcing themselves to laugh. Yes, there were some young people. Yes, we used to invite people, we weren't all the time cooped up by ourselves. Why did we stop? Because of the expense involved? Surely not, a glass of fruit juice here or there, a little biscuit. The biscuits we bought from Tripeau! I can still see them. They went soft in just a few days, we were fed up with them before we'd finished the tin. Was that why we stopped inviting people? So as not to have to buy those biscuits and waste the rest of the tin? Ask Gaston. I'm beginning to feel a little uneasy. Maybe it was because of me that we stopped inviting people? Gaston knew very well that it irritated me when I missed that toad and smelled the sweaty girls and had to hear for a couple of weeks about those biscuits we didn't eat. He knew it, so that was why he stopped going to the expense? In the long run, without wanting to, can't people be influenced by a sort of wet blanket, a sort of corpse that puts a spoke in the wheels, who's forever putting the brakes on any simple joy, who finds it hard to follow the crowd? I *must* find out.

Our guests would have suffered the repercussions, little by little, without knowing that it was my fault, and still smiling at me and carrying me along with them. Because they did still smile at that time. And little by little they stopped bothering about whether I was enjoying myself but the corpse was taking shape, it was beginning to stink, very gradually at first, like a little fart, you don't know where it comes from, you forget about it, but then it starts again, it continues, this time you've spotted the person. It's a false comparison because in my case they didn't know, they never knew where the smell came from. What they did know, poor things, was that the invitations became more infrequent and that one day there weren't any more. I hope I'm wrong. I hope this isn't the explanation. So I don't have that on my conscience as well. But I probably have. Let's say that maybe they too were growing weary and that the nieces were fed up to the back teeth with coming and missing the toad with those old fogeys. Let's hope so. They were growing up, they were finding other toads elsewhere, bigger ones, slobbery toads that they didn't miss and that gave them kids and that was it, they were married and the guest house became their childhood, they didn't want to remember it any more. Let's hope that that's it.

Courage.

I came out of the shed. Reber wasn't on her chair. Like the previous time. But this time, by wanting to annoy her, I had at least found something, that toad and the sadness that goes with it. In general, I never gain anything but the memory of something sad. Once again I told myself that she'd gone to pee or to get some different needles. I went to the kitchen. I didn't look at the time on the alarm clock. I asked Marie whether she had remembered the cheese. She said of course I remembered it, I don't rely on you to remind me what I have to do. Did she mean that I hadn't reminded her before she went shopping or did she want to get me to believe that I hadn't reminded her? That's easy, with me. To apologize, I said that's right, it was Monsieur Gaston who reminded you. She said ah, so I'm supposed to rely on Monsieur Gaston now, and who else? Why not Mademoiselle Reber while you're about it? She was angry. I changed the subject and asked her whether she'd seen my Therese Neumann, I must have left it somewhere, I can't find it. Your what? My book on Therese Neumann, I was reading it in the garden just now. She told me she wasn't in the habit of checking what I was reading, who's that Therese then, one of those sluts novels are full of. She was angry, I went out of the room. To avoid the trifle that would inevitably have followed. I went into the craproom to see whether I had put Therese back in her place, she wasn't there, I went out into the garden again, not there either. One more thing to find. But I couldn't have left it in the street, could I, when I was hiding from Reber? I went and looked. Gaston would be furious, I had to find that before my paper. I went back to the shed, I looked everywhere, in the aucubas, just in case I'd put it down while I was looking for my paper, in the craproom flower bed, in the refectory one, nothing. Reber came down again at that moment, I asked her if she'd seen it, she said no, didn't you have it on the steps, wasn't that what you were reading just now? I said yes it was, of course it was, I know very well I had it just now, that's why I'm asking you, why would I ask you if I didn't know? I was getting worked up, I shouldn't have. I went back to the craproom, it could only be in the craproom. Unless Gaston had picked it up as he went by? Where was he, where was Gaston? I went back to the refectory, he wasn't there, he must be in his room. I told myself don't let's go there, if he didn't pick it up he'll be furious. I stayed in the refectory. Marie came in to put away her dishes. It was at this moment that she must have told me about the wine. She set the table and as she put down a bottle she said there are only three left in the cellar, tell Monsieur Gaston will you. So I didn't go to the cellar for the bottles. Only for my paper. If it had occurred to me at that moment to go back to the cellar right away to check the bottles I might perhaps have found Therese. I went back later but it was too late, if Fonfon had been there he might very well have picked it up and then not known where he'd put it. Ask him tomorrow. Marie set the table. She asked me to push the armchair back against the window so she could get at the dumbwaiter. This chair is always floating around, it takes up a lot of space between the table and the window, we move it when we sit down. I sat down in it and thought stupidly about the nine degrees proof wine that needed to be ordered, mustn't forget to tell Gaston. I told myself that I preferred the eleven degrees. I got up, took my glass and filled it with the nine degrees, tasting it very thoughtfully. I didn't want Marie to say that's right, get yourself a good skinfull before lunch. I tasted it, making smacking noises with my tongue and palate and saying no doubt about it, I wonder whether we shouldn't order some eleven degrees, I don't much like this nine. She said personally I agree with you. She obviously suspected that we were economizing for the first installment on the machine and she wanted nothing to do with it, she was the one who'd get saddled with the work. To take Gaston's side once again I made some more noises with my mouth, poured myself another glass and said but it isn't actually so bad. This time she didn't miss me. Good excuse to get yourself a skinfull before lunch. Whether or not she knew that wine doesn't agree with me before a quarter to twelve, I didn't like that expected remark. I said Marie you're exaggerating, nine degrees proof. Precisely what I didn't want to say. I wanted to tell her to mind her own business and to watch her words. She went on setting the table with a nasty smile. She must be saying something to herself. She must suspect that in a very short time I shall have had a skinfull. That wine *will* agree with me before a quarter to twelve. Maybe before? Eleven o'clock? Eight o'clock? All the time? How can she suspect it? She knows me. She can see very well that I'm not getting any better and that this sort of thing always ends up in the booze. She knows something about these things, what with her husband who drank. He used to beat her up, that's why she divorced him. How right he was to beat her up. I can't even imagine how he could have lived with her. Her daughter couldn't, either, since she walks the streets. It's shrews like her they should have shoved in concentration camps. Gas-chamber, heave-ho. And salvage the bones to make into shit-house broom-handles. I'm getting worked up but it's true, she's been giving me a pain in the ass for so long, isn't it also because of her that I'm looking for my paper?

Repeat, I'm looking for my paper.

Mustn't lapse into vulgarity. It doesn't add anything and it runs the risk of falsifying things, you let yourself go and you no longer say what you wanted to say, you overdo it and lose the thread. It's Sougneau's daughter who walks the streets. Marie went out of the room, I stayed there with my nine degrees. I regretted having started so early, it couldn't have been a quarter to twelve yet. At that moment I saw Fonfon returning, he was coming through the gate. Reber looked up. The slap wasn't far off. He had certainly forgotten that he'd forgotten the chair this morning, Reber had only to remind him and once within reach, wham. I didn't want it. I quickly called Fonfon and went to the window. He told me he'd seen a duck on the river and had tried to catch it with a stone but the duck had escaped. I told him you mustn't keep throwing stones like that, do you think the duck likes it, would you like to be hit by a stone? He replied that he wasn't a duck. I told him come into the craproom with me, we'll look at a picture book. Reber didn't say anything, she'd slap him later on but at least I wouldn't see it. I went into the craproom with him and picked up the Don Quixote illustrated by Doré, always the same book. We start from scratch every time, every time with the same pleasure. Fonfon always gets excited at the same places. When Don Quixote puts the barber's brass basin on his head he bursts out laughing. And when Sancho is afraid in the forest, well, then... Because I go a little into detail, if you can call it that. Anything to do with caca is a real godsend. Incidentally, I wonder why people rack their brains to try to tell funny stories. Me and Fonfon, these are the only ones that make us laugh. And also when Don Quixote shows his behind to Sancho, obviously we find that funny. At one moment I told him you carry on without me be very careful not to crumple the pages. I went over to the bookshelves to see if I really hadn't put Therese back. I checked every shelf. I wasn't paying attention to Fonfon who had stood up with the book and come over to me, asking me something. I'd reached the very end of the bookshelves, on the right. Fonfon was in front of the chest of drawers, just a few centimeters away from the misery plant. I was on the top step of the little stepladder and when he asked me I turned around and I don't know how but I missed the next step down and fell flat on the floor. Fonfon bumped into the misery with Don Quixote and the misery fell out of its pumpkin. We were in a nice mess. The pot broken, all its soil on the floor. Reber yelled from the garden *now* what is it. I yelled back nothing, nothing at all, don't worry. Even so she came to the window, and she saw. I said as you see it's nothing, we only have to repot the misery with the soil that's there, Fonfon, put your book on the table. He was still holding it tight in his two hands so as not to crumple it. Put it down there and go and get me a pot from the shed, a pot this big, look, and don't let's get excited. He went. This was the perfect excuse for Reber to start bellyaching. This tradescantia which we'd been looking after for ten years, we might have saved ourselves the trouble, it's done for, broken to bits, might as well put it in the garbage can, you'll always be the same, you and your idiot. She came in, she added go and fetch me the dustpan and brush. I didn't like her tone once again. People who think they're indispensable when you get into a bit of bother and who just precisely are not. This almost always happens wth women. Do away with women. I went to the kitchen to get the dustpan and brush. Marie said *now* what is it, she hadn't heard anything. I said, nothing. Even so she came to see. She and Reber had a whale of a time. If things went on that way there'd be nothing left but the walls, only yesterday

my tea cup, the day before yesterday the soup tureen, what's Monsieur
Gaston going to say. I said and what about me, what might I say, I didn't
break that misery plant. I'd goofed, a slap for Fonfon, I smoothed it
over. And even if it was me, what's Gaston got to do with it, I'm in my
own home, aren't I? Who do you think is going to pay for the misery
and the cup and all the rest, Gaston maybe? I expect Gaston to pay for
broken pots, do I? And anyway there's absolutely nothing wrong with
this misery, take a look, I was holding it in my arms like a little baby, just
one little branch broken, and this little one here, while Reber was
sweeping up the soil, I shall re-pot it that's all, making such an almighty
fuss, and even if it *was* done for, well, I, I, you hear me, I would decide
not to replace it, it's hideous, having to look at that thing for ten years,
Gaston doesn't like it either. This wasn't true and they knew it. Marie
said we shall see, with her nasty smile, and she went back to the kitchen.
Fonfon came back with a pot that was much too big. Reber said I'll go
myself, I said no, let me see to it, you go back to your knitting. She
shrugged her shoulders, put the dustpan full of soil on the soiled floor,
and went out. Fonfon was crying. He said that old bitch Reber. I said be
quiet, I don't like you to say that, blow your nose, here, have my
handkerchief. He blew his nose all askew, not where it needed it, my
handkerchief was already full up and I didn't know how to fold it to
make a dry ball and put it back in my pocket, I put it down on the chest
of drawers and went to fetch a pot from the shed. I came back with the
ad hoc format and Fonfon repeated that old bitch Reber. I told him shut
your trap do you hear me? She's nervy, she isn't unkind, she knits for the
poor. Which I say to him every time he says that old bitch Reber. I added
and you'd be well advised to watch your step, you forgot her chair again
this morning. I re-potted the plant, you couldn't see any difference.
Fonfon wanted to water it. I said no, you carry on with Don Quixote,
I'll water it myself. I went to get some water from the kitchen. Marie
told me that the eggplants would soon be cooked, only another quarter
of an hour. So it was a quarter to twelve. I went back to the craproom
with my jug of water and watered the misery. I remember I said to
Fonfon that'll be its apéritif. Then I put the jug down on the chest of
drawers and went into the refectory and poured myself out a glass of
nine degrees. I went back to the craproom with it, saw the jug and the
handkerchief on the chest of drawers and told myself not to forget to
remove them, Gaston will make a scene. But where *was* Gaston? Still in
his room? That was impossible. Let me think. Where had I got to when

I was wondering where he was? And where was I? In the garden, probably. Around ten o'clock, before Marie came back from shopping. She comes back around half past ten. Did I go into the refectory around ten o'clock? Reber must have been coming down from her room at that moment. I said that she went straight out into the garden. Where was *I*? Near the gate? I remember that I said that I'd gone back into the craproom and that Gaston was going through his bills. No, that was at eight, I was coming down to drink my tea. After that I must simply have thought that he was still there, while I was maybe in the shed. Why did I wonder where he was? I'm lost. It's of no importance, it's of less and less importance. Must get ahead. This doesn't tell me where Gaston was while I was re-potting the misery nor when I was having my apéritif. Did he go out? While I was in the cellar? From the shed I would have heard him go out but not from the cellar. He might very well have gone out without Reber telling me. That's it. He was looking for a thriller for Apostolos, I saw that. It must have been on my third time down when I was telling myself that the way to search was to forget. Sit down on the steps and pretend to be reading so Reber wouldn't question me and from time to time look over the gravel for the little ball. That's it. What time, more or less? Probably about eleven. So Gaston must have gone out before that, otherwise he'd have had to step over me to get out. Or at least pass by me, I was on the bottom step. That *is* of some importance, though, it reminds me that I'm looking for that paper and I'm trying to forget it. Ask Gaston what time he went out. No doubt he'll tell me that he didn't go out but at least I shall have made the effort to remember. Mustn't let myself get remiss. Mustn't tell myself it's of no importance. And what about Apostolos? She didn't stay up in her room either. She isn't ill. Is she ill? No, she lunched with us. Where was she? At all events, not in the garden, of that I'm sure, only Reber was there. Did I see her in the refectory? Did I perhaps go in there before Marie set the table? Quite so, I did go there, to get myself that slice of bread and butter. But that must have been rather early. Yes, Marie insulted me with her 'trifle' before she went shopping, about half past nine. But Apostolos wouldn't have come down before half past ten. She usually sits in the little armchair in the corridor while Marie does her room. Unless she came down beforehand? That would amaze me. She must have come down at about half past ten or eleven. Then I have to draw the stupid conclusion that each time I went into the craproom she was hiding in the refectory and vice versa. Same applies to Gaston if he didn't go out. It doesn't make sense. I shouldn't have said all those names right off, I knew it.

All my wits, mustn't get worked up. I'm drinking my nine degrees, it's a quarter to twelve, I'm wondering where Gaston is. Did I actually wonder at that moment or only now, just a while ago? Yes, I did wonder, when I was telling myself not to forget to remove the handkerchief and the jug from the chest of drawers. I must have asked Fonfon if he'd seen Gaston and if he'd seen Madame Apostolos. Fonfon never knows anything. What did I do? I'm drinking my wine. I'm looking at Fonfon still looking at Don Quixote. I automatically look at the hulk, the mould on the wall, Eugénie. Eugénie. It's coming back to me. At one moment Gaston asked me to try to lower the print so as to hide the mould. When he was looking for the thriller? I went over to Eugénie, I climbed up on to the hulk, I couldn't reach the print, I told myself I'd need the stepladder, move the hulk and put the stepladder there. Fonfon asked me what are you doing. I said, nothing, we'll move the lady but not now, this afternoon. Just to break something else right away, thanks a lot. Marie shouted lunch is ready. I shall never discover where Gaston and Madame Apostolos were.

They were at the lunch table, though, neither ill nor somewhere else. She may very well have been feeling seedy this morning but have come down for lunch. And Gaston may very well have come into the craproom to get her a thriller to entertain her until lunchtime. But don't let's go back to all that.

Hold on, hang on.

We sat down to table. Fonfon had forgotten to wash his hands, I told him quick go and wash your hands. Reber said obviously, looking at pictures isn't going to get his hands washed. It's always Fonfon we send to wash his hands but we never wash ours. I don't, at least. It's pretty disgusting when you come down to it, I spend the whole morning pissing and at midday I cut the bread. But this must happen everywhere. In every family that eats bread. And that's not something that's going to kill anyone. That would be too much to hope for. Fonfon came back and Reber said show them to me. They weren't clean. She sent him back to wash them again. I told her even so we mustn't overdo it, we can't keep on at him all the time, he'll end up embittered, we'll never be able to do anything with him. She said he'll never change. Madame Apostolos unfolded her napkin and said but this isn't mine, it's Madame Cointet's, I recognize her lipstick, why haven't they been put with the soiled linen yet. Marie came in at this moment and put her dish down on the table. Apostolos asked Marie to give her her own napkin, you've given me Madame Cointet's, it ought to have been put with the soiled linen. Marie gave her hers and put the other back in the drawer. Fonfon came back. I told him to sit next to me, even though there's no shortage of space when there are only five of us. The rest of the year we are eleven. Those eleven gasbags busy masticating. Perrin is on my left, we share the end of the oval table, it took us a long time to find it in the sale-room, Gaston maintains that you can seat more people around an oval than around a rectangle.

On Perrin's left is Monsieur Cointet. He puts a cushion under his behind so as not to look too short beside his wife but it doesn't make a lot of difference, she's a head taller than him instead of a head and a half. They keep their pills between their two places and they're both always mixing up their boxes or tubes, every day there's some kind of fuss, she doesn't have her glasses, he can't see a thing in spite of his pince-nez, he brings the tube up to his nose, *she* holds it at a distance, finally she passes it to me and says are these really mine? Monsieur Cointet will always be the same muddlehead. She says Monsieur Cointet when she talks about her husband and they call each other *vous* in public. I know they call each other *tu* in their room, not that I listen at doors but they make a noise. Especially in the mornings. Cointet gets irritated because he can't find his suspenders or his specs or his handkerchief, he roams around the room, he farts in all the corners, he spits in the bidet, she gets irritated too because he's disturbing her in her game of patience. Every morning Madame Cointet plays her game of patience. She says ace king queen while Cointet farts in a corner. My suspenders, he says. Jack, ten, what? what did you say? My suspenders, I don't know where my suspenders are. Ten, nine, eight, have you looked in the closet? Cointet spits in the bidet, at least I presume it's the bidet as he's lost his handkerchief and the washbasin is always full of Madame Cointet's unmentionables, I know that from Marie. They aren't there. Have you looked under the bed? ace king, what did I say, had I got to eight, was it eight or seven? Seven. Ace king queen. Cointet yells they aren't there, *now* where have you put them? Madame Cointet gets irritated. Leave me alone, will you, I've gone all wrong because of your suspenders, leave me in peace, jack, ten, drat, it isn't going to come out, it's all your fault, why can't you remember where you put your suspenders, my patience won't come out. Cointet asks her what it was she'd wanted to know. She's forgotten. Should I or shouldn't I go to the hairdresser today. Did I say I should or I shouldn't, what did I say? And she goes back to her patience until whatever it is she should do. In any case, I can't imagine what the hairdresser does to her, her hair is done in the old-fashioned style, put up into a flat bun at the back and with two little curls in front, one on either temple.

In short, next to Cointet, his wife. On Madame Cointet's left, Madame Apostolos. She has her back to the window and it's extremely rare for her not to ask us to close it, even in July. She says it's draughts that cause rheumatism. She's been avoiding draughts for so long, wouldn't she do better to try to sit in one? Mightn't that cure her? She asked Marie before you go out would you please close the window, I hope these gentlemen won't be annoyed with me but my rheumatism you know. We were already in our shirtsleeves, we were already perspiring but we didn't say anything. Then she said that someone had told her, a lady had told her, that canaries were dying of the pip in the district at the moment. Do you think it's catching? An epidemic? What should I do with mine? Have it vaccinated? What can one do? I'm very worried. Gaston said he didn't know, nor did I. Reber said the poor things, the Good Lord's creatures, I must make inquiries, you did say the pip? Well yes, it seems so, the pip. I filled my glass. Gaston who had just tasted the dish said what's this, ratatouille? Reber said no, just eggplants without anything else. Gaston said without anything else? that's a good one, she hasn't forgotten the pepper. Just for once Gaston was saying something. I said, here, have a drink, and I filled his glass. And some bread, said Reber. If it burns your tongue, eat some bread, personally I find the seasoning just right, these things must have some taste, as an experiment Marie and I decided not to mix them with zucchini as usual, to make a change. Is it really too hot for you? Gaston said no just to get off the hook, these conversations irritate him and I'm the one who has to bear the brunt.

On Apostolos's left is Monsieur Vérassou. He's somewhere around forty. He's the youngest member of the guest house. Very polite, very clean. Just the slightest odour of the dispensary some days when he comes back from the hospital, which is more or less combined, again only on some days, with another odour which must be, and I don't know why I say this, that of chastity. But you must have an inkling of what I mean. In our institutions where there is only one bathroom for everybody and where we economize on hot water, we can't spend our whole time washing. I seem to remember that lust doesn't have the same odour, or that at all events it's much more disposed towards washing. Unless I'm completely off the rails. In short, Vérassou. A nice young fellow. He's more or less preparing a paper on his specialty. He does that in his room in the evenings when we give him too much of a pain in the ass. But one thing I can say frankly is that he's no less of a pain than we are. No conversation, not the slightest idea on anything whatsoever. On the other hand, he likes music. He always congratulates Madame Erard most warmly.

Keep calm. I'm going too fast.

Let's take a breath.

Let's look out of the window at the beautiful July night.

You can still smell the lingering odour of burned fat. The chestnut tree glints charcoal-grey. The Rivoires' house resembles a pagoda but a suburban one.

How stupid I am to write that, what's the point. Mustn't wonder any more.

How terrible they are—poverty, communal life, withering hearts. Simmering grudges. They will never erupt. Except in little splutters, in little dirty tricks. I've embarked on all that. It's too late to get out of it. I had ambitions, when I was young. I haven't mentioned that yet. I liked painting and music. When Gaston and I met again I admitted this to him. He understood, he told me that once we'd got settled in I'd have all the time in the world for my interests. And then, because I had all the time in the world, I didn't do anything. Fortunately I had the idea of botany. Must try to discover the name of Fonfon's little flower.

If I had to be frank about what really keeps me in the guest house apart from the obligation of staying there, I would say Fonfon. Just imagining that Reber could turn him nasty makes me want to kill her. Keep calm. I have all the rest of my life to look after Fonfon.

And thinking of Gaston again, that too distresses me. He's ageing. He still had a certain charm ten years ago, it's true, people used to call him the gentleman. What a change since then. He's like I don't know what, a retired sergeant-major. A displaced person. An insect in a can of sardines. Displaced, yes. A refugee. A refugee like Apostolos, like us all, in short. And in his eyes something vague, something hunted. That isn't the word. Something sad. Especially when he laughs.

On Vérassou's left, also at the round end of the table, there's Gaston. The table is too close to the dumbwaiter, either he or Vérassou often have to give Marie a hand. The dumbwaiter is in the corner to the right of the window. There are a whole lot of grease spots on the wall around it. We hung an oil painting in the Flemish style above it, geese with their throats slit, and onions. In my opinion this is the ugliest of all our pictures but Gaston likes it, it looks appropriate in a dining room. I look at it as little as possible. The other pictures we have, either in the craproom or in the bedrooms, aren't beautiful either, they come from the sale-room or from Gaston's grandmothers, but at least there's something pleasant or romantic about them, little portraits, little landscapes. Most of them are prints. I hope I won't need to describe them. On Gaston's left is Monsieur Erard. He's a rather tall fellow, with grey, slicked-back hair. I'm forgetting to say that neither he nor Vérassou are there at lunch, only in the evening. Vérassou lunches at the hospital and Erard on his rounds, he sometimes doesn't even get back in time for dinner, only after it, when he's had to see a client late. I hear him from my room when he comes home after we've gone up to bed or else I pass him in the corridor or on the stairs when I've gone down again to check the gas and the shutters. I'm always telling myself that I must get out of that habit but there's nothing to be done. Erard is always polite and unassuming. He looks particularly stupid because of his big nose and sunken mouth, just a tiny little chin. That's the most unattractive kind of face. He ought to try to grow a beard but he probably thinks it would make him look even older, the difference in age between him and his wife becomes more pronounced with age. He sits next to her at table and his wife is next to Fonfon who sits on my right. Monsieur Perrin and Monsieur Cointet are retired, they have all their meals with us. Perrin spends his time fishing or at the cinema and as for Cointet, I don't know what he does. He doesn't fish, in any case. Perrin goes fishing in the Manu, our little river. There's a lot of grass at the bottom of it, because of the sewers, probably. And floating cabbage stumps and dead rats which get stuck between the willows. There are bulrushes here and there along the river bank, where it's still damp, horsetails, and plants that need water. I am more interested in the plants in the woods. I go to Ferret's Wood, which is quite a way from the river, on the left bank. On the right bank the hills start, grassy at first, rather pretty, then they gradually become more arid, full of scrub and dead trees. A sad transition that has often given me nightmares. Of the kind that make you very glad to wake up. People who get lost or die in the scrub, Gaston who says he's going to see his mother, he takes a Tyrolean backpack full of apple jelly and I watch him going off with his handkerchief knotted over his head. I follow him with a magnifying glass as if I were studying a flower and soon all I can see of him is the white speck of his handkerchief, and then nothing at all. I know he isn't going to come back. Or Fonfon running after a butterfly or a bird, he gets lost in the scrub, we find a completely white carcass which is really that of an ox but I tell the others it's his, look at the tail. Stupid things like that which torment me. I don't go for walks over that way any more. I did go there in the beginning, when we were glad to have got settled in, but not any more. It's a place I avoid, as I said. No doubt a few years from now I won't be able to go anywhere any more, I'll be stuck at home. But I don't want to think about it. Everything that could get us out of our hole, give us something else to think about, but which actually drives us deeper into it. So that we can't even see the glimmer of a solution in the place where it might actually be. No, I don't want to think about it.

I've gone the rounds of the table. Marie went out. Reber spoke about her experience of eggplants, we masticate. Apostolos said, you see, she put the soiled napkin back in the drawer on purpose. I was afraid they were going to start talking about the laundry and the washing machine, I again asked Reber when she was going on holiday, whether it would be on the first of September as usual. She again said yes, she said some more about her niece and her nephew-in-law. And that she would try out these eggplants again, without anything else, to make a change from sauerkraut, they eat a lot of that in those parts, she does the cooking to give her niece a break. Her sister looks in every day while she's there and always finds a way to pick a quarrel with her, she again wondered whether she'd go next year, both my sister and my nephew are against me, what's going to become of me. Apostolos also started harping on her own theme again. That beautiful dress she wouldn't have a chance to wear this year, it'll be out-of-date next year, and to think of all that trouble Madame Erard and I went to, and a rather expensive material, you can find everything you want at the Magasins-Prix, these big stores really are very convenient, there weren't so many of them in the old days or else you made a point of patronizing the small shopkeepers so they didn't go bankrupt, these days people don't even think about it any more, they go where it's quicker and more convenient. She asked me whether I went there for my clothes, my shirts. I told her that I hadn't bought anything at all for quite a while, there's no point, I don't go anywhere, I'm wearing out my old clothes, they'll never wear out, I'm very light on my clothes, in one sense it's tiresome to wear the same things for years but in another it's reassuring and in any case it's economical. She said she understood me and she added with a smile that came from a long way back, from her youth, when she was attractive, gentlemen aren't clothes-conscious but ladies are. Take my dress, I absolutely had to have a new one, ladies like to follow the fashion. I saw the hippopotamus again in front of the mirror this winter. Or last winter? And the smile vanished. She wouldn't wear it this year and next year it would be out-of-date. I wondered what the difference was between the new dress and the one the old girl was wearing at the moment. Apart from the colour, I couldn't see any. I asked her. She told me that big flowers were still worn this year and they had put the buttons in front, you can see very well that these are at the back. Well, if the fashion changes next year, all she'll have to do is put her dress on back to front. But big flowers will no longer be à la mode. Then let her wear it now, at home. But first she wants to wear out the old one, which will never wear out, it would be a waste to wear the new one.

Fonfon dropped some eggplant on his trousers, a great big dollop. It wasn't of the slightest importance, his trousers are disgusting. But Reber was keeping an eye on him, she said that's it, another stain on his trousers. I leaned over to Fonfon, removed the eggplant and put it back on his plate, he ate it and wanted some more water. The carafe was by Reber. She said no, one glass is enough, it distends his stomach, he'll be ill again. I said these eggplants are very peppery, perhaps we could make an exception and give him another half glass. She said no, he'd had enough as it was, all he had to do was eat some bread. Fonfon was going to cry. Gaston can't bear that. He said pass me the carafe please, I'll give him half a glass and then that'll be enough, won't it, do you hear me, Fonfon, that'll be enough, blow your nose. I wanted to pass him my handkerchief but I didn't have it. I got up and went and took the dirty napkin out of the drawer. Reber yelled you can't do that. I said why not, it's dirty, I'll put it with the dirty linen myself. She was beside herself, blowing your nose on a napkin, who ever heard of such a thing, most appetizing, I congratulate you. I blew Fonfon's nose for him all the same and he drank his half glass at one gulp. I didn't know what to do with the napkin, if I threw it on the floor Reber would bawl it's a pigsty, we're living in a pigsty. I oughtn't to say either bawl or yell. Her voice becomes even harsher, even shriller, even more cutting than usual, in these cases, and it sometimes happens that her food goes down the wrong way when she's masticating. This is what happened. It looks as if she's going to pass out, she can't get her breath back, she has to raise her arms in the air, we're used to it and we just wait, but she always starts talking again too soon afterwards and it starts all over again. This is what happened because even so I had thrown it into the corner by the sideboard so it didn't get mixed up with ours a second time. Once again she was going to say pigsty and once again she choked. In the old days she used to leave the table double-quick but not any more, she raises one arm in the air and with the other she holds her napkin over her mouth, then she changes arms. When the fit was over she didn't repeat the performance right away but we'd got to the steak. Marie brought it in and said she wouldn't change the plates, that would give her too many dishes to do, she had to go out this afternoon. Fonfon couldn't manage to finish his eggplants, this time it would be Gaston who would lose his temper, I finished them for him. He looked at the carafe. I told him no very gently. When I say steak that's not altogether correct. It's a big bit of beef, the cheapest there is. Sougneau says it gets on her nerves to do it in thirteen pieces, counting the maids, she just cooks a big chunk and we do the best we can. Marie follows her example during the holidays even though there are only six of us at the most. I have a feeling it would be tenderer in slices but I may be wrong. It must be the quality that counts. In short, it's uneatable. We have bits of steak stuck in our teeth until the evening. The moment there's steak on the table we never stop trying to pick our teeth with our tongues, I can still see all those mugs deformed by a bulge, to left, to right. Perrin, though, goes at it with a tooth-pick, holding his other hand over his mouth. I often go at it with my fingers and I never know what to do with the piece I pull out, it disgusts me to eat it again. I surreptitiously put it in my napkin, watching Reber watching me. She doesn't dare say anything to *me*, even so, but the pigsty isn't far off, or Africa. While we're eating it we usually say that we ought to change our butcher, out butcher is taking us for a ride, the way he always palms his muck off on us, but Marie never wants to go to the other again, ever since he palmed an uneatable piece off on us. That was what happened, but even before we started masticating. It's Gaston's job to cut the meat. He tried to find the grain, but couldn't. I took a look. It was going in every direction. Gaston said this butcher is taking us for a ride, how long has he been palming his filth off on us, we must simply change. Apostolos said that a lady had told her that the other butcher was much better nowadays, Marie must simply go back to him.

She had already gone back to the kitchen. Gaston called her. How do you expect me to cut this, here, see for yourself, please don't get the meat from that butcher any more, you must simply go to the other one, it seems he's better than he used to be. He didn't employ so many circumlocutions this time, he'd had enough. Marie said what's the point, just so he palms his muck off on me, he hasn't changed, it's still the same, you only have to remember the piece he gave us, I couldn't even eat it. Gaston said it couldn't be worse than this one, still trying to find the grain, I tell you that Madame Apostolos says that the other is much better, a lady told her so, isn't that right Madame? Apostolos said quite so, a lady told me that she used to go to our butcher, that he only gave her uneatable pieces of meat, but that she's just changed and it's like chalk and cheese, she's amazed that we still go to this one. Marie said the lady could say what she liked, *she* knew what would happen if she changed back, maybe that lady buys more expensive meat, that's why. Apostolos said I tell you it isn't, she buys steak. Marie lost her temper. Steak, steak, there are dozens of different kinds of steak, if I bought a filet obviously it would be better, don't you realize that that lady buys filet steaks. But Apostolos repeated steak, steak, just like us, the proof is that she's changed her butcher. Marie went out banging the door. Gaston hacked up the meat, we each had our chunk which we started masticating. While we were arguing Fonfon had left the table, saying he was going to wash his hands, I knew he was going to get a drink of water from the kitchen faucet. Reber told him to stay at the table but it was too late, he'd scrammed. He came back through the corridor door after Marie had banged hers. His shirt was soaked through. Reber produced a pinched smile, she didn't want to re-choke, she merely said educational principles there's the result. Or did Fonfon go out before Gaston called Marie back? Yes, before. Immediately after he'd gulped down his half glass, while Reber still had her arms in the air. I told him be quick, telling Reber his hands are covered in eggplant, he'll get it all over the place, let him go. When he came back soaked I didn't so much as look at Reber, she could say what she liked, and it was at that moment that Gaston called Marie back. Or just before, when Fonfon was still in the kitchen, and he came back while Marie was losing her temper, because I wondered whether Marie had thought that Reber was saying fine educational principles about her. Yes, more likely that. In short, we were masticating our chunks. Gaston told her to bring in the salad right away, that would make it easier to choke it down. I said I'd rather go myself, give her time to get a grip on herself, she might well throw it in our faces. And I went into the kitchen. Fonfon was there, I saw him drinking from the faucet. Hell, I'm mixing it all up again. Our meals are like that every day. I saw Fonfon drinking from the faucet, I told him hurry up, it was while he was hurrying up that he soaked himself. We went back into the refectory together, I pretended not to hear Reber and her principles, I said the salad isn't ready yet, she's just making it.

Repeat, of no importance. Gaston must have said well then we'll wait, picking at a top left-hand tooth, the hollow one, I've been telling him for I don't know how long to go to the dentist, he answers that it doesn't hurt. We'll wait.

As a rule, when we're talking about the butcher Madame Cointet says to her husband do you remember the roast beef in the Borromean Islands. They went there thirty years ago, a long time before they came to us. In Isola Bella, the menu on the twenty-fifth of June, I can't remember why, and the roast beef that melted in your mouth, and the dessert, and the flowers on the island, the trip on the lake, and it goes on with Lugano and Montreux. And when they get in a muddle, when they say one thing instead of another, they're corrected by Reber who has never been there but who knows the tale by heart. It's a long time since anyone has intervened at this moment, we let them talk, it gives us a break. I look after Fonfon, I cut up his meat for him, and I masticate my own and think about what I've lost on that particular day, or I repack my bag. To hear these Borromeans spoken of as if they were the Hanging Gardens of Babylon, and to hear those three old fogeys clucking over such marvels, mulled and re-mulled, ruminated and re-ruminated, digested and all the rest of it, all the while picking their stumps full of our loathsome grub — this inspires me. The life they had before, at all events the Cointets, which comes back and takes the place of this one with such precision that they can almost smell the flowers and taste the menu of the twenty-fifth of June, isn't that exciting? And even more so for Reber, who knows only Alsace and sauerkraut, that I have the impression, not only me but Gaston too, that she has come to believe that she has actually been to the Borromeans. All this is side by side in my head with Reber's sewing-bee in paradise, with the stupidity of people who travel, with the memories that drive us to distraction, the obsessions, the suicides, the failures. It's a sad bag that I pack. So I unpack it. I can hear all this buzzing around in my head while I'm unpacking my bag, I feel disgusted with myself, I pour myself a glass of wine. But it has the opposite effect on the Cointets and Reber, it puts new life in them. Madame Cointet almost gets some colour in her face and she unconsciously adjusts her chemisette and her brooch as if she were smartening herself up to go for a trip on the lake. Next Reber says it's like at home in Alsace, and she talks about the sunflowers or potato flowers they have there, about the storks and the first communions. It's the Cointets' turn to have a break. Next Apostolos usually talks about her own travels which have almost always been exiles but they were so long ago that we can hardly believe in them and I don't think anyone listens any more. Yes, Perrin does sometimes catch her out when she confuses one historical fact with another and then it's his turn to talk about Suez and the Stavisky affair, please excuse the chronology. When I've finished unpacking my bag we've got to the salad.

Sometimes it's Vérassou who takes over, on Sundays, I mean, or in the evenings, when we're treating ourselves to the left-over meat fancied up into an omelette or meat balls. He talks about what he's seen at the hospital, or about what people have told him there, the incurable cases, the amputations, the road accidents with details which personally take away my appetite or what remains of it but not them, not in the least, especially the ladies. Like mustard or gherkins, it makes them salivate, they ask for more, they want more details. They masticate their lousy meat and lick their chops. Is their subconscious imagining it's chomping on the sawn-off leg or the amputated bollock? Oh yes, they adore road accidents. I remember that one afternoon in the craproom Apostolos was saying that a lady had told her that she'd seen I forget what, a mangled body on the road, and she was beginning to tell us about it when Reber said but that's my accident, I've just read about it in the paper, and she wanted to tell it herself but Apostolos wouldn't let her, they were having tea, the biscuits hadn't been brought in, Reber was on her feet to pour out the tea and she went to fetch them from the refectory leaving both doors open so as not to miss of word of Apostolos's errors, she shouted from the refectory while she was putting the biscuits on a saucer no that's not it, he didn't die right away, and she was still going on when she came back with the biscuits, and when Apostolos had finished she started again, I'll tell you what it said in the paper and the others went on swilling and nibbling as they listened to these horrors, all the time saying how horrible.

We'll wait. Do you remember the Borromeans. The whole thing started up again. First I cut up Fonfon's meat and then I foundered.

Much more than usual, much deeper. There was no point in going on. I felt I was even worse than a puppet or a clown, I was a swine. I was still getting them to believe that the only thing I was interested in was my botany, that I was forever obsessed with looking for something, that I was a harmless eccentric. That I had seen nothing whereas they had been to the Borromeans, that I kept quiet because I could see very well that they had lived, that they knew life, that we owed them respect, that I was taking them as an example. I could no longer go on lying like that, they deserved respect, yes, but not the sort they imagined. I ought to tell them once and for all that their Borromeans had never existed, if they had been what they said they were they wouldn't say it any more, they'd have forgotten them, they'd have shat them out with all the rest. The very fact of going on talking about them proved that they hadn't understood the first thing about them, that they had been somewhere else when they saw them, in their phony, fair-ground paradise which was slipping through their fingers, that they were nothing but pathetic creatures of both sexes and that at this very moment, while they were going for a trip on the lake, there was only one thing they were afraid of although they didn't realize it, and that was of ending up the way they actually were ending up, and that was why they closed their eyes when they were contemplating the azaleas. Difficult to say that that proved it but you know I'm right, it couldn't be otherwise, unless you were a Madame Cointet or a Mademoiselle Reber. And even them, wouldn't I be able to put them on the right track? The caca track, where however much you stuff yourself with roast beef and azaleas, everything has the same taste. That was the respect I owed them. I had to say something and I was considering what. Or else more gently, to make it a little easier for them, so I didn't see them change colour right away, they'd have time for that later, when they were in bed. I considered. And I said the precise opposite. I said to Reber I apologize about the napkin, it was because I didn't have my handkerchief, it won't happen again. Marie was bringing in the salad. She said what, what napkin? I showed her where it was, I told her that I'd put it with the dirty linen myself, don't worry, I needed it for Fonfon. What, you wiped him with that? Blew his nose, I didn't have my handkerchief, it won't happen again. There was a fine shemozzle. She still hadn't stomached the business of the butcher, this finished her off. That we were all pigs, all the lot of us, that she was working herself to the bone for... I've just made a mistake, the Cointets are on holiday, there weren't any Borromeans this lunchtime.

But it comes to the same thing. Apostolos must certainly have talked about her own roast beef, shoving her top denture up with her tongue, or she was thinking about it. Personally, whether or not the Cointets are there, I always hear the Borromeans. That she was working herself to the bone for pigs, that we didn't care a damn about her, that we treated her like dirt, the whole works. And she went out again, banging the door again. Reber said obviously, blowing people's noses on napkins isn't going to put her in a good mood. Gaston said that's enough, that's not why she's angry it's because of everything else, and especially because she isn't on holiday yet, she wanted to take her holiday in July but Madame Sougneau had to go because of her niece. She's very nervy, she gets tired, that's the way she is. He retrieved the bit of steak from the top left hand side of his mouth with his tongue, but *he* swallows it. And one thing leading to another we started talking about the laundry again and naturally about the machine. Because of me, I was the one who'd started it off again.

On second thought, I now think that I've just said precisely what I didn't want to say, after my bag. When I apologized about the napkin I wasn't necessarily trying to shove their noses back into their squalor. I may well have told myself after all why always make a mountain out of everything, why contemplate my navel the whole time. If I'm dishonest what does it matter, if they think me this or that what does it matter seeing that their Borromeans give them pleasure, they don't get so much as all that after all. Why don't I encourage their non-Borromeans, I mean the little aggravations we carry around with us? These too help them to live, since they are still breathing. Or even systematically force them to talk about the machine again? In the final analysis, it isn't an aggravation for them, it would make a change, couldn't they wallow in that the way they do in the azaleas? Even Gaston however much he says that it's a lot of money to lay out, it entails more work for Marie and an explanation to the laundress who will be furious to see our dirty sheets and dish cloths vanish? For him it's a kind of adventure, maybe he tells himself that he must be a good person to fret about all this, just in order to be modern, and active? The farther I go in my exposé the more I see I'm right, this is certainly the truth. Then don't let anyone still ask me to be logical, don't let anyone tell me I don't know what I want. I want nothing. Less than nothing.

The salad didn't have enough seasoning. Marie hadn't put the oil and vinegar bottle on the table. I went and got it from the sideboard.

The thing with two spouts, I don't know what it's called, it had plenty of oil in it, too much, even, it was greasy from top to bottom, but no more vinegar. Oh dear, I said, there isn't any more vinegar, I'll go and get some from the kitchen. I went there. And that was where I saw a terrible thing, Marie crying while she was masticating her steak. She didn't even pretend to wipe her eyes or to be choking, she didn't look at me, she didn't stop masticating. I pretended I hadn't seen and took the vinegar out of the cupboard. I held it over the sink so as not to get it all over the place and I filled the thing. I told myself I must say something to her, I must find something, I can't leave her crying like that. And the thing overflowed. Marie yelled that's right, pour the whole stinking lot down the sink, then they'll say I'm the one that wastes all the stuff. I was saved. I took the vinegar back to the refectory. She's crying, I said to Gaston. He said then she'll piss less. It didn't affect him in the least, nor the others. Did they want to imply that it was none of their business, that it was all my fault? I shut my trap. Gaston made some more vinaigrette and Apostolos said not too much pepper, please, there was quite enough in the eggplants. Reber repeated that they were very good. Fonfon was squirming on his chair. I told him in a very low voice go on, go on right away, it'll be too late after. He went out. Reber said he's going to get another drink of water, I suppose? I said no, to evacuate it. Help yourself to salad, I'm not having any. I've never known whether I like salad. Sometimes I feel like it, at other times it almost makes me want to vomit. I don't know what it depends on. At all events I do know that I don't like hard, crunchy romaine lettuce with its big veins. Nor endive, either, you don't know how to eat it, there's always a spiky bit that gets up your nose. It's regular salad, ordinary lettuce that I'm not sure about. This oughtn't to worry me but it does. I like people who have decided tastes, you know where you are with them. You say to yourself he doesn't like that, I won't give it to him, or the opposite. It's reassuring. One thing at least that you know. With me, it's not only that I don't know but other people don't either. They aren't sure whether they should pass me the salad, they ask themselves does he want any, they're just about to help themselves first and then they think better of it, they pass it to me timidly and say some salad? They don't even say some salad these days, which would imply that they know that some days I feel like salad and other days I don't. They don't even know that much about me. Should I quite simply explain to them? Yes, but the explanation, thanks a lot. This one wouldn't be enough, I would realize that only too well as I was giving it, I would try to touch on the reasons and then we would immediately get to the causes, I can already hear myself concluding that I don't like salad when I've heard the swallows twittering in the morning, and that I do like it when it's going to rain. No, musn't explain to them. And as if she was doing it on purpose Reber who hadn't heard that I wasn't having any asks me aren't you having any? I wasn't yet thinking about what I've just said, I wasn't tormented, but I said well yes, after all perhaps I'll have just one leaf. And I choked it down, but I had to have a swig of wine on top of it. I'm sure people think I exaggerate.

This meal bores me much more than it bores those who are reading about it. Now I'm making them read at the same time. Than those who *will* read about it. But I must follow it through to the end. Precision and discipline. Take advantage of the opportunity. And then, I can't bog myself down in botany, specialize exclusively in amateur botany. I'm getting to the point where I no longer regret having lost that paper. Mustn't forget that I'm looking for it. That gives me something to do. At least I have that. Must do it conscientiously while it's there. After, we never know what's lying in wait for us. The future, that's what's lying in wait. It's dripping, it's shitting. Must watch out for vulgarities. It's true, though, the future is like the runs, it drains you, it kills you. I'm afraid of the runs. I don't want to think about it. A tiny little future no bigger than that, which I wipe away, which I toss off page after page, that suits me. No expectations, no overall pictures, the lightest possible baggage. To make me feel just a little bit good for once. My hand, writing and gently tossing off the future. I mustn't go too quickly. I must go quickly, I must finish before tomorrow. Find a way to extend the limit, to say that tomorrow is the day after tomorrow. No, mustn't say anything. Not for the moment. Gently, tenderly, toss off the little future.

I passed the salad back to Reber, she helped herself and passed it on to Apostolos who helped herself and was just starting to eat it when Fonfon came back from the crapper. His trousers were soaked, he'd done it all over them. Apostolos's fork was full of salad, she was just about to wolf it down but she stopped short, I can still see her. However dirty Fonfon's trousers are, it shows, a big patch like that all the way down. She didn't say anything because she isn't spiteful like Reber, she pities him. But I turned around and I saw. Sit down. But Reber had seen too and she said this time no, he won't sit down in that state. It's one thing for him to blow his nose in our napkins but for him to cover our chairs in that, Monsieur Gaston, say something. Gaston said what, what's the matter, his mouth was full of salad, I can still see him. I said he got his trousers a little wet, what of it, we aren't going to make another song and dance just for that. Reber said a little wet, a little wet, they're soaked, that's what they are, but say something Monsieur Gaston. Gaston turned around to Fonfon and said well let him go and fetch the floorcloth, he can put it on his chair. But I didn't want Marie to know so I said I'll go, you stay there. Marie had stopped crying. I took the floorcloth from under the sink as if it was quite natural but she said now what is it. I said, nothing, just a few drops of water I spilt on the floor, don't move. This time she didn't come to see. I went back to the refectory but Fonfon had already sat down again, Gaston could see that he'd been going to cry. I told him stand up and let me put this under you. He caught the tablecloth as he stood up and the wine turned turtle, on the oilcloth first and on the floor next. Reber was about to choke, she put her fork down on her plate and clenched her fists on the edge of the table. Apostolos went on tucking into the salad. I said it's nothing, actually it's fine, I just happen to have the floorcloth, and I started mopping up the wine on the floor. Fonfon was going to cry. Gaston told him sit down and eat. He helped him to salad. But I had to wipe the oilcloth too, there was nothing within reach, I didn't want Reber to pass out if I used the floorcloth. So what did I do? I quite simply took the napkin from the corner and mopped up the table. Reber didn't say anything, she got up and walked out. This happens to her sometimes, often, even. Either she takes her plate into the craproom, quickly taking another helping as she goes, or else when we've got to the end she says I'm not hungry any more, I'll wait for you for coffee. It would be better if she did it every time, before she starts choking I mean. But in that case she would never eat anywhere but in the craproom. I put the floorcloth and the napkin in the corner by the sideboard and that was that. Fonfon said she won't have any dessert, serves her right. We didn't react.

After that Marie brought in the cheese. So it was true that she'd bought some. I asked Gaston whether it was he who had reminded her. I had to ask him. That's enough. They ate their cheese. It was just as well Reber had gone out, there wasn't any blue. I didn't want any cheese myself, I wanted to puke. It had begun with the snot in the napkin, and it gradually became more specific. I poured myself another glass of wine while I was waiting for the coffee but it didn't make any difference, nor did the coffee, the feeling persisted throughout the afternoon and evening. They say it comes from the liver but I doubt it, there's nothing wrong with my liver, the doctor told me so. He's an old doctor who knows nothing but I have confidence in him. I've already spoken about him elsewhere. I've even said he was dead, to try to get rid of him. No, not of him, but of the obsessive fear of his death. That's the sort of thing I do for the people I like. I imagine that they're dead, I kill them, and I'm free of their anguish.

Must try to say something exquisite, to neutralize the vomit. Half-witted subtleties, recipes for fruit pies or cream caramel. Maudlin scruples, acts of kindness fit to make you sweat. What could I possibly say that was exquisite? I mustn't look for it, it has to come out spontaneously. It was on the tip of my tongue to say something of the sort just now, but what was it? It'll come back. They were eating their cheese. Cheese sticks worse than steak, I realize this with Apostolos, her denture goes click-clack, no, not click-clack, something much more subtle, when she's eating cheese. She pushes it forward with her tongue to get at the bit that's got stuck and I rather think she brings some steak back with it. Or is it backward? She said this cheese isn't as good as the last one, it can't be the same piece, it's a pity we can't always count on getting the same quality. And then she suddenly corrected herself, probably thinking about the scene with the steak, that is I suppose it isn't, but even so it's really very good, the cheese of this quality that my niece buys can't hold a candle to it, what is it, gruyère or Franche-Comté? Now I come to think of it, it isn't possible for her denture to make more noise with cheese than with steak, I heard it more with the cheese because I wasn't myself masticating. I replied gruyère probably, you only have to ask Marie. Gaston was casting a vague eye at the window, he was going over his sums. It was so hot that I asked Apostolos if we couldn't open the window again. She said of course, look, I'll take Mademoiselle Reber's place, and she moved round to the end of the table. More exactly, I opened the window first and only then asked her is that all right, she said yes, I'll take Mademoiselle Reber's place and she got up and sat down again nearer the end of the table, where she thinks there isn't a draught. The Rivoire wall was blinding, we kept getting intermittent whiffs of burned fat, it was as if we were in the bowels of a ship. I don't need to repeat that the month of July makes me give up the ghost. They say this is often the case with people who were born in that month, and it *is* my case. I can't wait for August to come though it hardly makes any difference and after that it's September, the summer's over and we regret the summer no end. It's a bit like salad, I no longer know whether I like the summer. I know that I'm ill during July, as I am at the moment, I have to admit that I'm ill, and sometimes I feel better in September but then once again the dog gets harnessed to the plough, as they say, they all come back from their holidays and it's worse than in the summer. I ought to be able to manage to discover whether I'm less ill in September than in the summer but it would be difficult. I'd have to be at one and the same time in July and in September to be able to make the comparison. Because at the moment when I imagine September I do so without exactly imagining all the shambles of the homecomings and the sadness of getting back into the habits which we've never really got out of, two months' holiday, that doesn't count, I say to myself roll on September, but once it has come I think less about the ghastly July light, the main thing I see is the mugs of our guests and I regret the summer when we were more peaceful. I ought to call July September and vice versa, maybe it's just a question of words after all, the ghastly September light, that doesn't sound right, I wouldn't be able to say it any more so maybe I'd see it less? But at that moment what would I call the month of August? The ghastly light would move into August, I'd be iller in August than in September, and I'd find myself back in July and I'd once again be saying the ghastly July light, not seeing that it's softer in September, and I'd be ill all over again. Yes, it must be a question of words but don't let's change them, that would make it worse. And besides, even if it wasn't worse, all alone in my corner I couldn't say in July it's September it's September, there'd always be someone who'd be saying can you believe it, aren't we having a wonderful July, which would deflate me and make my temperature shoot up which would make me iller still because I wouldn't have been prepared for it, or else when I was asking Reber when she would be going on holiday I wouldn't have been able to say at the beginning of July as usual, I'd have no alternative but to say at the beginning of September, and that would force me back into July in which we would in fact be and heave-ho, my temperature shoots up again and this might well be the knockout blow. I'm not over-keen on that, I don't like death, as I've already said, and that isn't the least inexplicable thing. If I had to remake myself I'd be hard put to it. But I think I'd try to be born in January, when people are numb with cold. Problems with the guests and problems of the heart are the same but maybe less burning. I say that because I'm thinking about them from a distance. No, one does at least look forward to *something*, to see that spring will soon be here again, I tell myself that I'll soon be able to go for my walks in the wood again. What's more, I wouldn't even know that the horror of July existed since I should have been born in January. Unless there's a January horror for the people born then? Not worth thinking about. The best thing would be if I never looked forward to changing the months, never looked forward to anything, to any future. But I've just said that. The little future, the minuscule future, that's all there is. Repeat: the little future. To foresee, a minute before, that you're going to get to the bottom of the page, that's all I can allow myself. It's lamentable but there's no other way. I would like there to be someone, at least someone, who understood the state I'm in but I know very well that that's impossible. Let's forget about it. After the cheese, the peaches. We stuff ourselves with peaches all through July, they're what's cheapest. I quite like peaches but I can't gorge myself with them like Apostolos or Gaston. You ought to see how they put them away, it's nauseating. One, two, sometimes three. They're not bothered, they're what's cheapest, they're as common as dirt, people all but run after us in the street to sell us their peaches, a bit more and they'd give them away. No, personally I take one and sometimes I can't even finish that, I see Gaston looking at the half I've left on my plate and he looks at me, pursing up his lips, he shouldn't because it's hardly even a waste, given their price. But he can't help it. And he says since you aren't going to finish it I'll have it and he devours it. That makes three and a half for him. His excuse is that he's nursing his intestines, as I've already said. If he isn't careful he can't go often enough. So he stuffs himself with peaches. And in August it's melons that are as common as dirt and then he stuffs himself with melons. Even half of one for a first course and the other half for dessert. He's the only one. He has melon for his first course if we're having it for dessert and melon for his dessert if we're having it as a first course. Those slow intestines are unbearable. He must think back with delight to his Sirancy diarrheas but as I've already said that didn't change a thing, he's blocked again a week later, wasn't worth while going to all that expense, with me it's the opposite, I wasn't going so often in Sirancy when I met him, I only stayed there a few days, I was passing through, but even so I realized that I wasn't going so often. This isn't interesting but it's suddenly occurred to me, maybe that explains why I'm not on the whole mad on fruit, my organism is protecting itself without my help. In the final analysis, what *am* I mad about? What a bore, don't let's start again. Yes, though, I'm mad on strawberries but there's no likelihood of their upsetting my stomach, they're always too expensive. We have them two or three times a season at the outside. At the height of the season when they're likely to go bad the shopkeepers sell them off cheap. At the end of the season they're expensive again just like at the beginning, I'm not giving away any secrets. And if by chance Marie has bought a lot for once then I pitch into them with the result you already know, but so what. In any case it doesn't last, my organism knows this too and it does its bit, they don't really upset me. Not liquid for three days as it might well be. In short, though I have no particular desire to go too closely into the matter of my physique, this might be the one way to find myself a friend. Somewhere round about the spleen, for instance. A place that likes me and that knows the business of the strawberries that don't last. But it would be painful to dwell on one's spleen, just the very thought of it depresses me. Let's forget about it. They stuff themselves with their peaches, sucking up the juice, making that disgusting noise to stop the juice dripping into their plates. Gaston, not Apostolos, she eats her peaches with a fork as they did in the old days. Gaston eats them in his fingers, skin and all, and he sucks the stone so as not to lose the slightest bit, all the while looking into the middle distance, he's going over his sums. Even so he gets juice all over his fingers and wipes them on his napkin and Marie raises hell because it apparently makes terrible stains, the only ones that won't come out. That's where they've got to. Apostolos is peeling her first peach. She does so slowly, she takes her time, already spotting the one on the dish that she's going to take for her second. She has a good eye, she doesn't make mistakes. She just feels it with her fingertips and it's always the right one. First peach. Slowly. She puts the peel and the stone on the edge of her plate, the stone a little farther back, it would roll over, and she cuts the peach with her knife. The sugar. Always some sugar, to make the ensuing disgusting mess you're going to see. There's something else that is as common as dirt while I'm thinking about it, and that is artichokes in the spring. This has something to do with the country you live in, if we were in Africa or I don't know where, we wouldn't have any artichokes. It's incredible that in the times we live in we still haven't managed to get rid of this plant. So when they're in season we eat them all the time, we tell ourselves they're good for the liver. Marie brings them home by the bushel, whole basketfuls of them thinking she's economizing. To watch them being eaten is even more disgusting than all the rest. They all nibble their leaves down to the very tip, they all but bite their fingers off, not that they like the stuff, at least I don't suppose they do after all this time, but they've got into the habit, they nibble them down to the tip. This irritates me so much that the moment my artichoke is on my plate I pull off all its leaves at one go, whoosh, burning my fingers, then I blow on them and to get rid of them I dip the whole tuft into the sauce, eat the tips and that's that. Reber looks at me and thinks that it's a pity to let things go to waste like that. I'm committing artichoke sins. If we just ate the hearts, if Sougneau prepared us a dish of artichoke hearts, that wouldn't be so bad, the hearts are quite a delicacy in their own way, not all the time, of course not, but they're more of a delicacy, but no, out of the question to leave the leaves, for a couple of weeks we never stop piling artichoke leaves up in the dish, whole mountains of them, and the garbage can is full to bursting point with artichoke leaves. It's really painful to think about, it's frightful, but what can I think about, what? That we should eat pineapples? That would come to the same thing, it would be the pineapple leaves and stumps that we'd be tossing into the garbage can and I'd be committing pineapple sins. Shit. It's revolting. Life is revolting.

Soon coming to the disgusting mess but not quite yet. She dips her pieces of peach into the sugar and they go down, and how they go down, it looks as if she's swallowing them whole. Then she puts her fork down and takes the peach she's had her eye on out of the dish. Does she actually put her fork down? No, she doesn't. She still has it in her hand when she picks up the second peach which she barely fingers, it's the right one, and heave-ho, she picks up her knife and she re-peels. Skin on the edge, stone a little farther back, re-sugar, re-dip, re-swallow. Then it's the next one. If I look too hard at her she stops, this is usually the case but not always, as I've already said, and she holds out her glass for someone to pour her a drop of wine, just a tiny drop for my little tidbit, she drools over it, she loses her denture in it, my little tidbit. This is the disgusting mess in question. She pours the tiny drop, almost half a glass, on to her sugar in her plate and stirs it with her spoon. Marie gives her one for this especial purpose. She drinks the juice out of her spoon, she sips it. For my part I'm not looking at her at this moment, it's impossible, but I can hear. By this time Gaston has sometimes got to his third peach, he eats them more quickly because he doesn't peel them but in between he's thinking, he's re-doing his sums. Today it was his third. Or his fourth? I'd left half mine on my plate. Glance, pursed lips. Since you aren't going to eat it. And he swallowed it. Apostolos hadn't finished her juice. We left her to finish it and went into the craproom for coffee. And Fonfon? What had he been doing all this time? Did he have a peach? I can't remember. Or maybe he took it out into the garden. That must be it. He often has his dessert in the garden, this is a relief for everyone, we let him do what he likes. Unless it's a rice pudding for example, Sougneau is mad on rice pudding, rice gâteau as it's also called, or rice dessert. I don't like bringing this up again but honestly, and precisely, this is the one thing I can't eat, it makes me vomit on the spot. It used to, when I was small. I haven't tried it since. I never eat it. But it provides one more opportunity for me to feel sick when I watch them, I don't always find an excuse to leave the room. I ought to. There's no point in accumulating bitter feelings against everyone. Our poor guests who can't help it. Our poor Gaston who torments himself about his machine. Our poor collaborators, that's what he calls the maids, one more circumlocution, who can't find polka-dot dresses and black silk coats at the Magasins-Prix, reticules with chains and shoes with straps, nothing but hideous stuff, and who cry in their kitchen because they aren't on holiday, because their niece is a bitch, because their daughter is a streetwalker, and so on. Yes, I ought to. From now on I shall leave the room the moment I see the rice pudding on the table. Or rather, in the winter I shall ask Sougneau every day what she's going to give us for dessert and if it's that I shall leave the table even before it appears. But I shall have forgotten what she's told me, I shall mix it up with yesterday. I shall leave the room at the time. Must remember this winter.

When he came into the craproom Gaston said what's all this muck, seeing my handkerchief and the jug on the chest of drawers. I said, nothing, I'm sorry, I left my handkerchief there by mistake just now, the jug was to water the misery. I darted a glance at Reber who was waiting for a chance to get her own back. She's so spiteful and so virtuous that she said it's wrong of you to say that. Gaston said why. I had to explain that I'd knocked the misery over and repotted it, you can't see a thing, look, barely one little branch broken, it's just as it was before. He looked at the misery and said one, two, three branches broken, it's a terrible mess, how did you do it. I looked at the old bitch who was getting a hell of a kick, all the time pretending to be knitting, I had to explain the whole thing to Gaston, that I was looking for a book in the shelves, that I was on the stepladder. He asked me what book. I said Therese

Neumann. He said obviously you couldn't find it you stupid jackass seeing that I'd taken it for Madame Apostolos. At this moment she came into the craproom and said what, what have I taken. Gaston said not you, me, I gave you Therese Neumann this morning. She said yes, I haven't had time to read it yet, it's sure to be very interesting. But in that case what book was I looking for? Up to now I've said Therese Neumann to simplify matters, I already knew it wasn't that since Gaston told me so after lunch but before that I believed that it *was* Therese, when I was looking for it, but when I said that it was, I was naturally putting myself in my own place, I was looking for Therese Neumann. And I wonder now how I could have believed I was looking for that book since Gaston had taken it, since I'd seen him take it, or rather he'd told me I'm looking for Therese Neumann for Apostolos, not a thriller. I must already have got things muddled at that moment, and thought he'd told me a thriller because I was the one who wanted Therese? Why did I say I'd taken just any book, Therese Neumann for example, or rather why did I have the impression that I'd taken just any book, Therese Neumann, or rather that I *had* taken her, that I'd taken her out on to the steps? That's my nature. Such a state of nerves that I attributed to Gaston what I meant to say myself. Let me think. Where was I when I wanted to get a book. I think I was by the window in the craproom, and I saw Gaston getting a book. I must have asked him what are you looking for, he must have replied Therese Neumann for Apostolos. I must have said to myself at that moment, and in any case I *did* say it, huh, good idea, it gave me the idea of taking a book too to pretend to be reading so I could take a look at the gravel from time to time without Reber asking me what I was doing. That was it. Right. I go into the craproom and I say to myself Therese Neumann, Therese Neumann, good idea. And it was at that moment that I got them confused, he was taking it for Apostolos and I was looking for it for myself, that's my nature all over. I was so pleased with the idea he had given me that I took *his*. Not to be able to rely on myself is distressing. Must tell the neighbour. Not to have any more wits about me than that, taking what other people say to you for what you say yourself. And all the time I was sitting on the steps I thought I was reading Therese whereas I was reading a thriller. Just as well I wasn't reading it. But why could I still hear Gaston saying thriller to me? I must have heard it afterwards, since I wanted Therese so much, it must have been me telling myself he's taken a thriller or something of the sort for that old goose, I'll treat myself to Therese, I've been wanting to read her for ages, that'll give me one more mystic in my baggage to mix up with the others. That has to be the way it was. I hope it won't go any farther, farther than the steps, I mean, I don't feel up to saying it all again, remembering it all again, starting all over again. It gave me quite a shock when he said that to me but I pretended it hadn't, I said what an idiot I am, you told me this morning, but you see I was looking for it all the same, and Fonfon, well I mean I was thinking about Fonfon, I was wondering what he was doing in the garden and I turned around abruptly I don't know why and I missed the step below and wham, I knocked the misery over. I was keeping an eye on the old bitch who looked up and said it's wrong of you to say that. I couldn't let Gaston think I was a liar so I said to Reber do you by any chance take me for a liar, I know what I do, don't I? She said with a smile that was just asking to be bombarded with shit, that is not what I meant, oh no, but you see Monsieur Gaston, I was in the garden and I know that the idiot wasn't there and when I heard a commotion I went to the window and he was there, where you are now, he was even holding Don Quixote, no one else can have knocked over your favourite plant. I didn't lose my head, I never lose my head where Fonfon is concerned, I said to Gaston and what if he was there, it was still me that took a header and knocked over the misery, wasn't it? He said don't look at me like that, I don't know anything about it, I wasn't there. I said well then, believe it or not, that was how it happened. I was on velvet. Reber hadn't seen me fall either, nor that it was Fonfon who had knocked their shit over. Given her virtue she couldn't contradict me but even so she said if you go on excusing him and humouring him like that you'll make him impossible to live with, there'll be nothing left of this house but its walls. She'd already said that to Marie. So then I really lost my temper and I said well even were that the case, I remember I said well even were that the case, one more expression to use to the neighbour, well even were that the case that nothing was left but the walls, that would still be more than you deserve. She didn't choke because her mouth wasn't full, she didn't leave the room because she wanted her coffee, she... She did what? I don't know any more. At all events she shut her trap so I was able to carry on explaining to Gaston. That we'd been to get another pot from the shed and that I'd put the soil back in that and repotted the misery. At this moment Marie came in with the coffee and did she prick up her ears, she was getting all set to get a kick out of it too. I saw her look at Reber as white as a sheet, that's what she was, as white as a sheet, she put the coffee down on the table and turned around to us. At that moment I thought let's put a stop to it, let's deprive her of her orgasm, let her go and jerk herself off in the kitchen. And I said nothing. I told her thank you Marie, you may go. But she didn't go. Gaston said come on then, spit it out. So I had to carry on. Where'd I got to. Repotted the misery. And I said to myself let's water it, that can't do it any harm. And I went into the kitchen and filled this water jug and came back to water it and there you are. And the handkerchief, said Gaston. I replied, don't you get into the act too if you please. I left it there because it was full, I couldn't roll it up into a ball and I forgot it, I'm sorry. Marie was lying in wait for me to get her revenge for the napkin. It wouldn't be that you blew Fonfon's nose with it as he was crying because he'd knocked over the misery? She wanted to carry on, to carry on until Gaston exploded so she could then say to me in front of Reber, between her and Reber and me, and what's more you said that Monsieur Gaston doesn't like his plant, you've just seen, you've just seen. But she did after all have to go and finish herself off in the kitchen because Gaston had had a bellyful, he wanted his coffee, he sat down in the Cointet armchair and said right, thank you Marie. I was very pleased.

The Cointet armchair. Describe a piece of furniture, to make a diversion.

It's on the right of the hulk, beside the little Moroccan table. It's upholstered in piss-coloured plush, piss-yellow, with fringes and tassels, one more horror. It really does belong to the Cointets, when they moved in they brought what furniture they had left which we put in their bedroom or in the others or else in the craproom as for example their chair and other things that I'll mention when the occasion arises, when I can't bear it any longer. When they're here they don't lend it to anyone, it's Madame Cointet's place. If her husband sits down in front of her at a slight angle because of the table to hold her wool for her we can be quite sure that either he when he makes an awkward movement or she when she winds her wool too fast, or pulls to the left because he's holding his arms crooked, will knock over the little lamp on the table or in any case just by touching it put it out or make it flicker, there's a loose connection somewhere, we never remember to repair it. Her husband stands up and gets the whole skein in a tangle as he either picks up the little lamp or pushes the plug back in and Madame Cointet says perhaps we ought to call the electrician, it can't be anything much. I ought to be able to fix it myself. Remember lamp. While this is going on we are all busy, Gaston is going over his accounts, Reber is knitting, Perrin is searching the cupboard for a cutting on the Dreyfus affair, Vérassou doesn't know what to say and goes up to his room, Madame Erard has come down from hers with her dolls and she goes over to the bookshelves to have some room and spreads out her pile of rags and ribbons and old bits of material, or she unpicks a ragged old knitted garment to get some frizzy wool, this makes the dolls' hair, Erard when he's there dozes on the hulk and I, if I've told myself let's be pleasant, I play bezique with Apostolos who always gets the cards wrong, she marries the king of spades with the queen of clubs, or she declares bezique although it's the opposite, queen of diamonds and jack of spades. That's how we spend our evenings.

Reber had poured out the coffee. One lump of sugar for Gaston, two for Apostolos though she would actually prefer three, two for me, none for her. She points this out every time, the fact that she doesn't take sugar. Gaston was already sitting in the Cointet, she handed him his cup, then she handed me mine, I was sitting by the table and put it down on it. Apostolos said and what about me? It's coming, it's coming, says Reber, here, and she handed her her cup. I could easily say that one of the cups got knocked over but what's the point? Should I rack my brains to make people laugh? If it wasn't today then it was yesterday or before. You'll notice that Reber was no longer sulking, or if she was she was concealing it, she's so afraid that I'll pour the coffee myself, or Gaston, she thinks it's her privilege, she awarded it to herself, it would be like getting a slap in the face if we were to do it because before, it was Apostolos who poured the coffee but now her hand shakes, she's as blind as a bat, and when we saw that things had got to that state we poured it out for her and told her there's no need for you to go to all that trouble. Reber doesn't want this to happen to her. But I wasn't thinking about that, I was thinking about Therese Neumann, or I was starting to think about her, to wonder how it had happened, and about my little ball in the gravel, and about Fonfon, we couldn't hear him, was he up the chestnut tree. When we're having coffee I think about several things at the same time, I let myself go, it must have something to do with digestion. Of no importance. I am sitting near my cup, I can see Reber re-knitting, I can hear Apostolos re-sipping and Gaston snoring gently. No effort to make conversation after lunch, no bills, we relax. It's especially in the afternoons, this torpor, whether it's hot or cold, July or January. I oughtn't to say that Gaston snores, he dozes off and it's as if he misses, how can I put it, it's as if he misses one breath out of two and then catches up with it at the last minute, this makes a little noise that comes from the back of his nose, it's not very loud, not that awful snorting sound that sets your teeth on edge, just a murmur, and irregular at that, mingled with a little hissing sound, I can't find the right word, produced by his saliva which either can't go down because he's holding his breath or trickles out in front and makes him dribble. When he got into this habit, it was quite a few years ago now, but before, at the start, he didn't doze off—when he got into this habit I was ashamed vis-à-vis the others and I used to cough to wake him up but I don't any more, not for quite a few years, none of them gives a damn and it would be very stupid of me to deprive him of this moment of well-being, when he isn't thinking about his bills. But it still has an effect on me, not of shame any more but of pity, which is worse. Especially when I imagine the way I myself must look when I'm asleep, but at least no one sees me. And in spite of this at least, I tell myself that this is one of the things that I regret, not that I regret, since I don't regret anything, but which still makes me suffer at my age, not to have had anyone, or so rarely, in any case not to have anyone any more who watches me sleep. So I'll draw a veil over the pity I would inspire and the shame I would feel afterwards when I discover that I dribble or that I snore. Especially as I know perfectly well that I do dribble, sometimes my pillow is completely soaked in the morning. But I know very well that I'm analyzing everything because it bores me to go back to thinking about what I was thinking about before. And yet I must. I was certainly thinking about Therese Neumann, I was beginning to wonder how it had happened, I was a little worried, for some time now I've been telling myself that things can't go on like that, and I was seeing the little ball, yes there was the little ball, no mistake about that, I was telling myself that I could see it on the table, caught up in the mesh of the crocheted mat, it was as stupid as that, I found it there, or under Apostolos, in the slit of the blue armchair, it had slipped down into the slit between the seat and the back where you always find things, a cigarette lighter, pins, I'd have to look there, or maybe Fonfon had put it there for fun or without realizing, maybe while he was looking through Don Quixote and I was on the stepladder, and at the same time I could see him finding the paper in the chestnut tree and putting it in the empty chaffinch's nest, I haven't asked him whether he'd seen anything, must ask him. And that that little ball or that paper could be everywhere, in corners I

hadn't even thought about, my afternoon was going to be fully occu-
pied. But I've still forgotten something. Before I left the table, when
Gaston had finished his dessert, I said to Apostolos who was finishing
her juice, Marie has given me the number of a temporary help, it could
always come in useful, did she mention it to you. She said no, I'll join
you in the salon. We left her there and went into the craproom. When
she came in, then, she said to Gaston what have I taken, when he was
talking about the book, and then she sat down in the blue armchair.
When Marie had gone out after putting the coffee on the table she
remembered my question and asked me what was all that about a
temporary help. I said I'll talk to you about that later, it was none of
Reber's business. I looked to see whether there was any reaction from
the old bitch but I couldn't see her expression, she was in three-quarters
profile, pouring out the coffee. In any case she didn't say anything. But I
thought back to her connivance with Marie, forgetting that it was
hardly likely, because of something else between them this morning
which I've forgotten. And while I was still seeing my little ball and
Apostolos's slit and the chestnut tree I was vaguely mulling over this
plot between Reber and Marie, I was hearing Reber telling us really not
worth it, needless expense, I'll take care of the housekeeping as I did last
year.

    This is becoming more and more insipid. But I must carry on, even
so. It's when you've given up hope that the miracle happens. I may quite
likely find something that has nothing to do with my paper, and even
less with my life, which will put me on some sort of track. I'm already
making a note: slit, blue armchair, I forgot to look this afternoon.
Something unexpected, something dazzling. And even if it doesn't
result in my finding my paper, so what, I'm not going to resign myself
to its loss, oh no, but I shall also get interested in that dazzling thing.
Maybe it could cure me of my constant queasiness? Change me? Trans-
form me? Then a new me would come out of that trifle, a being who
was all pure, all grace, all smiles! Sometimes it almost seems to me that I
have only just missed it, that if I hadn't been obliged to let myself get
embroiled in our existence I might have become that being and that he's
still lying dormant somewhere, in limbo, maybe in my body but
whatever happens I mustn't look for him, mustn't concentrate on my
spleen, I must go on talking, dissecting ineptitudes, forcing myself, and
then you never know one more thing that I might also force myself to
say, which has nothing whatsoever to do with that being, might all of a

sudden make him appear, shoot up like a rocket. Yes, I'm thinking about it seriously, I would never have thought I would have to say it one day it's so stupid, but that's the truth. I still haven't come to terms with it. That's to say that I have really, but there's still something else, at my age, that preys on my mind, which is that I can't say no. So impossible, so stupid, that I'm not even on my guard against it so it's still budding, or rather seething, or let's say shivering. And this probably does me a lot of harm, however indifferent I am to it, however much I ignore it most of the time, and fart on it, my organism probably knows something about it and by trying to ignore it I'm going against my organism and the splendid creature is dying of tedium. I'm waffling at the moment but at least I shall have mentioned it and I still say that this will go on troubling me whether I like it or not. To find myself one day stark naked on a beach drawing up the plans of the Acropolis! Or, I don't know, distributing to children the traditional baptismal sugared almonds of my christening, I'm going to be in sole charge of my life, no embroilment, I shall be at the helm of the ship. Always that idiotic ship, that ultra-phony metaphor, but how can I shake it off now, I've had it inculcated, intravenoused, stuffed into me. I've been stuffed with this ship which is joggling up and down in my behind, it's horrible when I come to think about it. Mustn't think about it any more. And must stop being vulgar.

Grrrrr. Here we go. Gaston wakes up. He opens a pink eye and stretches, in the Cointet. He doesn't pretend he hasn't been asleep, he isn't a gentleman any more. He says what's the time and it's always twenty to two. Already twenty to two, he looks at his watch. He said this afternoon I shall have to go. I asked him where. He said various things, I'll tell you, and the plumber, I'm sure Marie's forgotten again, did she go. I said no, though I didn't remember, but she was sure to have forgotten. And then suddenly, seeing Gaston stand up, my heart missed a beat, it hurt, more than usual. There was that light, that heat, that smell of burned fat, the Rivoire wall that blinds us, Apostolos and Reber slumped down like jellyfish in their armchairs, and there was I, having to spend the afternoon like that, in our squalor, for the whole of July, for the whole of my life. Fits of depression worse than the others, and inexplicable. And even just thinking about it now plunges me back into it, I can't go on.

I *am* going on. I went the rounds of my room, looking under all the furniture, but this time automatically, like a robot. It's only now that I realize this. And I looked at the ghastly night outside. The owl has just hooted. It eats the rats scampering around, we find their gutted skins in the garden. It must live on the other side of the street, in the roof of a disused barn, beyond our neighbour's house. This owl soothes me, I wouldn't like anyone to find its hiding place and chase it out. Hard to say why it soothes me. I'm going to come out with a lot of nonsense.

It soothes me because I have a kind of feeling that it's there when we aren't, as if it was mounting guard while we're asleep to see that nothing gets eaten by the rats, that everything remains in order, so that we'll find everything in order tomorrow. No. I'd like nothing better than for the rats to eat up the whole of the garden and the guest house with it, for us to find nothing left of it or at all events total chaos, not necessarily caused by the rats, by something else, shadows, nightmares, the horrors of the night, such total chaos that we'd be forced to put all our guests in the poorhouse, shut up shop and go and live in the country. So it isn't that.

It soothes me because I have a kind of feeling that it knows I'm here at my table, it sees my light, it hoots at me, don't worry, I'm here too, you aren't the only one who's struggling, there are two of us struggling to rid the garden of its rats, maybe it thinks I deal with the rats too, but in that case I wouldn't be giving it any pleasure, there'd be less of them for it to eat, it isn't a friendly hoot, it's an insult like fish-face, mind your own business, eat your eggplants and leave the rats to me, and I tell myself that it's right, I forget that I'm not looking for rats, or rather that I'm trying to track down the rats of the heart, the foul rats of the heart, maybe that, it has to be that, forgetting that *it* couldn't do that, it's not its job? Yes, it must be that, but then it can't soothe me, on the contrary, I'd be riled if the owl thought that, and I'd try to disabuse it of the idea, to calm it down by putting my light out. In which case I would be soothing the owl, so it isn't that either.

It soothes me because I have a kind of feeling that things become transformed when it hoots, that everything becomes rather pleasantly owlish, rather flighty, rather ratlike, the garden shivers to make its rats jump, all the attics of the Rivoire pagoda are looking for something, such as eyes in the anthracite of the chestnut tree, the neighbour's weathercock tries out a maneuver, it wants to go off to the seaside or somewhere else, in short there's movement everywhere so long as the owl is hooting, the moment it stops everything will return to immobility, the owl keeps us alert, it disturbs me, I feel exhilarated, feverish. So it doesn't soothe me. On the contrary. It isn't that either.

It soothes me because I have a kind of feeling...

What a bore. I knew it would be a lot of nonsense but I was still vaguely hoping that I might come up with a gem without really meaning to. It didn't work.

I must start again in the craproom. The anguish I felt when I saw Gaston stand up. What did I say to him? Yes, don't forget the plumber. He told me that Marie had remembered, he was coming tomorrow. I told myself that she'd remembered because I had reminded her but I didn't say it, I'm modest. I said to myself well yes, if I wasn't the doughty owl that does away with your rats for you... Cretin. Fatigue again, probably, fatigue once more, what can you do against fatigue? You can tell it to go to hell, that's what you can do. I don't want to sleep. I don't want to. To have to start this exposé all over again tomorrow, I shan't understand the first thing about it, I shall have forgotten everything, no, it's impossible, no, I don't want to. I shall stay on it like a child on its pot, he keeps trying to get up, his mother looks to see whether he's done anything, he still hasn't done anything, she sticks him back on it until he produces the goods. I want to be the child, the pot, and the mother all at the same time. I sit down on it again and when I'm full I shall call out I've done caca. This word always gives me renewed courage, as you may have noticed. Long live caca. And it's just too bad if I'm repeating myself, if I'm revelling in it. This is my own truth, this is my strength, this is my banner. Long live caca. I seem to think I'm at the Feast of Corpus Christi now, what with my banners. But I don't give a damn. I feel better. I'm in great form. I'm going to become a live wire. The fit of depression? It has just hit me much harder now, remembering it, than it did this afternoon, I did momentarily feel something but very rapidly, just in a flash, and I didn't stay sitting there contemplating my jellyfish in their armchairs, nor that light, the blow had fallen and I would carry it with me until the evening and throughout the month and throughout the year, yes indeed, but I didn't start pampering it, I'm too used to that, people simply don't understand me if they think I drive myself silly brooding over the blows of fate, far from it, they pamper themselves independently, they relish themselves independently in my insides, for my part I go on doing something, I get over it right away, I act, you have to act. I stood up after Gaston and went out on to the steps while he was going up to his room to fetch something, I told myself I'll wait for him here and when he comes past I'll ask him what he had to do at the same time saying to myself I just hope it isn't the washing machine but I wanted to know, we *are* partners after all, just because I'm no longer up to it that's no reason for him to treat me as a nobody, I exist, don't I, I'm a human person, a failure, that we know, but who is nevertheless *there*, who realizes it, who realizes that he's a failure but who suffers from that fact, who suffers martyrdom, who does everything he can to make it easier for people to put up with him, however much he says he despises everyone and privately calls them stupid cunts, he never says so to their face, he treats them with consideration, he smooths things over, is it really true that my not being up to it can be taken as a pretext to consider that I no longer exist? That would be too much to hope for, that would be too simple, they have just as much of a duty to put up with my failure as I have to put up with theirs, they're all worms, crawling carcasses, starting with Gaston and well yes, what does he think he is? What does he think he's invented? Just because he keeps the accounts? Just because those cuntesses side with him over the misery plant? Even so that would be too easy, too simple. I'll tell him what he is, and this minute, at that, when he comes down he'll take his beret from the hat stand, he'll put it on his head, then he'll find me on the steps and he'll walk all over me as he did this morning or else detour around me as a matter of form, purely as a matter of form, and I shall tell him what he is, just like that, between the craproom and the garden, on the steps which from that moment will have become his Waterloo, as they say, it will knock him rigid, root him to he spot, he'll collapse on to the ground, his muscles will sag, he'll start foaming at the mouth, he won't know where he is, he'll have lost consciousness, I shall leave him in that state for as long as it takes me to remember what I wanted to say to him and when I've remembered I shall lean over him and instead of slapping his face and applying a damp cloth to get him to open his eyes I shall say into his earhole failure, it's failure I wanted to say, you're a failure do you hear me? Just because you make such a song and dance about buying that machine, that rotten, common or garden machine, everyone has a washing machine these days, it's no novelty, it isn't something you've invented, you haven't invented anything, you hear me? nothing at all, and if those cuntesses side with you over the misery it isn't on your account, it's to get their own back on me, they don't give a damn about you, all they think about is themselves, they think they're less unhappy when they're getting their own back on me but do you really think they are? pah, that's crap, pure crap, do you hear, all this time and we still haven't managed to make a go of this lousy guest house, do you think they don't realize? that they don't realize that it's definitely because of you, they've known for ages that I'm not up to it but they relied on you, they relied on you much longer and then all of a sudden, before they can say knife, they find themselves having to face the obvious fact that you're a worm just like anyone else, a crawling carcass, nothing to hope for, they go on pretending to side with you because they've got into the habit but it would only need one word from me, one word do you hear, I'd only have to lift my little finger and they'd do an about-face and side with *me*, quite so, with *me*, and wouldn't you like to know, eh, what it is, that little word, that little finger I lift, well, I'm not going to tell you, I'm keeping it in reserve, I'm keeping it to myself, do you really believe they're interested in your machine? Not Reber, she's against it, but Apostolos and old mother Cointet and Madame Erard and all the rest, do you really believe that? You're an innocent, what an innocent you are, a vain little man, a vain, insignificant little man, I'll tell you why they pretend to be interested in it, for it *is* only a pretense, quite simply the reason is that it gives them something to talk about, even Reber at that, something that in a way flatters them because they think it's modern, because it's expensive, but do you really believe they're stupid enough not to realize that we shall never buy it? Don't you realize that after all this time that we've been trying to do something, to modernize the place, to redecorate it, to buy new furniture, we still haven't succeeded, we shall never succeed? Redecorate the place! Buy new furniture! You really amuse me! And to think that me too I used to believe in it, even until just a short while ago, well yes, I rather think that's what I said to Reber, to get her to leave us in peace next July, quite so I really did tell her that, well, isn't that the limit, as if we'll ever manage it, as if we'll ever have the wherewithal, as if we'll ever have the energy! Can you see us redecorating, getting up before dawn, brush in hand, and repainting the whole wretched shack from top to bottom? No, really! You'd have a ready-made excuse, you'd have to be going over your sums for the washing machine all day long, all month long, and I'd be left to do the whole damned thing on my own, wouldn't I? Just to start all over again in ten years' time? No, you make me laugh, you really make me laugh. And to redecorate the place, have you even imagined what that would entail? We'd have to go through everything, all the crap in the attic and the cupboards, all the Hermes statuettes, all the little clocks, your beloved little clocks, your adored little Carpeaux, your little grandmothers who've been giving us a pain in the ass for the last ten years on top of the cupboards and everywhere else, in all the bedrooms, go through them, sort them out, and put them where? Because you really imagine you'd want to get rid of them? Don't think I don't know you! You'd want to keep the lot, not throw anything away, put everything back in its place, or rather try to find a place for everything, as if we hadn't already tried a hundred times, a hundred times, don't I just remember! We'd start trying to find somewhere to put them all over again, we'd get the same ideas we've already had a hundred times and which were no good, we wouldn't remember, we'd re-hump all your crap from bedroom to bedroom to see if they'd go in and they wouldn't go in, no room, and then what would we do? We'd go and put them back in the cupboard, in the cupboards, and when we saw the oil lamps and the plate-warmers we'd tell each other that they're pretty, they're works of art, antiques, we can't just leave them in the cupboard like that, it's a sin, now I'm talking like Reber, we can't just leave them in there, it's a waste, we must be able to see them, such pretty things, things they don't make any more, they're valuable, aren't they? And we'd take them out again and once again try to find a place for them but where, on the sideboard impossible, on the dumbwaiter impossible, on the table impossible, on the catafalque impossible, in the craproom then, under the misery maybe? Change the pumpkin for the bottom of an oil lamp or a plate-warmer? We've already tried that but you don't remember, we didn't know what to do with the pumpkin, do you think we'd know this time? Can you see us in the middle of all this clutter? Don't you realize that we gave up the idea of redecorating long ago, just putting all the stuff back where it came from would take us the whole day, we wouldn't remember whether we'd tried that adorable little Houdon on the piano, between the vase and the hookah, it didn't go there, it was wedged up much too close to them, and we'd re-try and we'd re-give up and we'd re-start with another adorable little thing and in the evening we'd find ourselves eating our meat-balls in the middle of all this jumble which we'd once again have to put away tomorrow, no, no, and no, you really make me laugh! Really, you know, I feel sorry for you, then it happened, I *was* sorry for him, I was done for, he opened his eyes and I was sorry for him, I said oh come on now, don't take it to heart, it had to come out but basically you know very well that without you we'd have closed down long ago and they'd all be in the poorhouse, we rely on you you know, you're indispensable, more than indispensable, vital, vital, I said vital, when had I said that before? Apropos of what? I shall have to discover, to remember, in short he stood up, I put his beret back on his head for him and forgot to ask him where he was going.

I'm exaggerating, am I? I'm making fun of everyone? I shan't answer.

I followed Gaston out of the room but he didn't go upstairs, he took his beret from the hat rack, put it on, and went out. He could tell me tomorrow what he had gone to do, or the day after, or never, it was all the same to me. I could imagine anything I liked, I might be right every time, it didn't interest me. It couldn't be so very sensational, even if it was the machine he could buy it if it gave him any pleasure, we'd deal with the installments like we deal with all the rest, what difference would it make? Why had I just asked him what he was going to do? Out of habit. If I'd taken a leaf out of Barbey d'Aurevilly's book and asked him whether he was going to bugger the pope and he'd said yes, that was precisely what he was going to do, it wouldn't have worried me one way or the other. In the first place it wouldn't have been true, and even if it had been true, or possible, even if the pope had been within reach and I'd known it, or thought about it, what difference would that make? Here I really am exaggerating but there are moments when we have a right to exaggerate, it acts like a safety valve, it gives harmless vent to our spleen. I've just seen the connection between the word vent and what I said about the pope, it was quite involuntary. I often think about these free associations. Connections, things that resemble one another, which are very close and you don't know it, no one knows it, and you come out with them just like that and a whole world, a whole universe is revealed to us, abysses, hells. I've chosen the wrong moment to talk about these serious things, after what I said about the pope, but please forget that and concentrate on the abysses fate opens up, not abysses, things we didn't know about but which suddenly start moving under our eyes or rather under our ears but our ears begin to see and because they can see so well, all life is there within reach, all our poor infectious worm's life which gives us so many headaches is exposed there, we can hold it in the hollow of our hand, it was just a little bird, nothing at all, how could we have made such a song and dance about it? Difficult to talk about that, very difficult. But I notice that it's always words that reveal this sort of thing to me, it's always free associations, couplings or comparisons, it's always that. That's why I say that certain things, as I've just said, I've forgotten which things, may perhaps be nothing but a question of words. What I'm saying here is important, very important. For me, of course. Where'd I got to. Gaston going out of the gate. I watched him go out, I watched that old man, no other way to describe him now, with his beret on his head, going out of the gate into the street and even farther, two hundred meters, three hundred meters, who passed his whole life passing through that gate merely to go three hundred meters farther away to do something he had to do which would turn out to be nothing, absolutely nothing. Yes, I thought about him. Rapidly or not rapidly, in a flash or not, I thought about him, it's coming back to me. This old man that I'd known for ten years, that I'd got to know again ten years before—I didn't know him. I could tell myself what he was going to do, I could imagine no matter what and it would probably be right, though utterly useless, I'd known that for the last ten years, yet I didn't know him. Just because I knew his reactions and could always foresee them, even act as his prompter, and that has happened, there have been occasions when I have prompted his reactions unbeknownst to him, and presto, reaction, just because I could do that didn't mean that I knew him, wasn't it rather the opposite? I suddenly told myself that it was the opposite. It's because I know his reactions that I don't know him. The precise opposite of what people usually say. But I'm used to that, to the opposite of what people usually say, and which visits me. Yes, visits. Or announces? Announces. So I'm the Blessed Virgin now. I was going to blaspheme again but I pulled myself up in time, I don't give a damn what people think but no one can think anything as no one knows what it was going to be. I'm used to opposites and the idea that I didn't know Gaston didn't particularly surprise me. At the moment, yes, for a quarter of a second, a quarter of a second later I was already used to it and I was saying to myself, it's true, I don't know why it's true but I don't know him. And I saw the neighbour's gate and the weathercock and the scarecrow. And I told myself that Gaston, he's the neighbour, that fellow I want to speak to but that I'll never speak to and that I imagine I'm speaking to and who fills my life with completely phony conversations but who in a kind of way keeps me alive, you can almost say keeps, no more than all the rest of course but no less—that's Gaston. And I again had what they call a presence, I certainly had a presence at that moment, there was no one in the garden, Reber must have been having a siesta on the hulk, when we aren't there she abandons her knitting. I imagined, it must have been at that moment but if it was at another so what, that moment would have been the most appropriate, I think, that Gaston and the neighbour were the same chap, that we didn't know anything about the neighbour because he was Gaston, and that he was perpetuating our ignorance the better to preserve the confusion. And so the neighbour was Gaston. He'd bought that house without telling me, he'd put up that weathercock, that scarecrow, he was spreading the rumour that he was a retired railroad employee and that was it, that was why nobody knew him, nobody had ever spoken to him, it was as clear as daylight. Since he was never there, since we didn't see him. But what was it that Gaston used to say when someone asked him who the neighbour was? What was it he used to say? This goes back a long way because no one asks any more now. Or could it be that they don't ask any more because Gaston has let them into the secret? Could he have told them his secret so as to stop them asking, so that I wouldn't hear any more talk about this neighbour? A secret they shared, against me? What does it mean? What is this latest mystery? Is that where the cat hurts its paw? In the neighbour's garden? Why am I always thinking about cats? Is it a sign? Am I surrounded by cats and signs? Am I caught in the net? Are they going to strangle me? Get away! Get away, with your filthy cats! Keep calm. Keep calm.

Oh come now, it's impossible, Gaston can't have done that to me, why would he have done that? What advantage would it be to him? I'll tell you what advantage it would be, what horrible advantage. He keeps a houseful of whores over there and he organizes orgies, that's the advantage. The pig! Organizing orgies for ten years under my very nose, wallowing in filth under my very nose! No no, though, we mustn't get worked up, he isn't a swine, I'm not against lust, I'm perfectly prepared to admit it for other people, so we mustn't get worked up. Yes but I am, I *am* getting worked up, yes but I am, I *am* against it, I don't admit it for anyone, he *is* a swine, quite so, I won't put up with it, I won't put up with having put up with it, I'm going to the police this very minute. The bastard, doing that to me! And under cover of his fatuous air, his mincing manner, his accounts, his moronic worries! The unspeakable bastard. That's it, isn't it? Admit that that's what it is, that you've been organizing orgies in that house for the last ten years without telling me! Admit it, go on, admit it! The police, the police right away.

My caca has put me into too good shape, I'm talking utter rubbish. But what if I were right? If I were suddenly discovering this horror without meaning to, if that was the mistake? You never can tell, you never know. That's the point I've reached.

All my wits. Start again from the beginning. I can't let myself go like this, it's impossible. Keep calm. Courage. Start again from the beginning.

I got up at eight, woken by Marie. She knocks on my door three times. No point. Just start from the siesta. He's snoring gently in the Cointet. There. Mustn't lose my head. I'm thinking of the effect he makes on me and I'm telling myself that I'm quite right not to wake him up, no one gives a damn, I can see Reber knitting, and Apostolos, what's she doing? She's in the blue armchair and her head keeps dropping a bit farther, a bit farther, she pulls it back, barely opening an eye, it drops again, that's it, she's snoozing too. She's digesting her eggplants and her steak and her salad and her cheese and her peaches and her tidbit and her coffee, that's quite a lot for just one female. Even so, can't she just stuff herself. Not surprising that she has rheumatism, it clogs her limbs, her joints are all fouled up with cheese and lovely sugar. Poor woman. Did I wonder what she could be dreaming of? I think so, yes. I must have wondered whether she still dreamed of lust. Just the very sight of that pathetic, crumpled-up mug dropping down and snoozing, with her head full of pictures of lust and youth—it breaks my heart. Maybe at that moment she opens her legs? No, no smut. Maybe she's rereading a love letter from an admirer inviting her to Nice? Maybe she's making herself a dress with flounces and lace and fal-lals? For the ball at the Prefect's Residence? No, that's even worse. I mean sadder, not smuttier. Sadder than any kind of smut. Better to think that she either isn't dreaming at all, or else only about a vague canary that's bringing her news of paradise. She takes the love letter from the vague bird's neck and finds inside it a sweet-smelling rose which tells her your exile is over, my darling, all over, we're entering paradise. And she picks up the train of her wedding dress and enters paradise. Yes, I like that better.

Gaston wakes up and stretches. Twenty to two. He looks at his watch. Twenty to two, I must go. I didn't ask him any questions, perhaps that surprised him, and he said I have various things to do. Still didn't question him. Among other things, the plumber, he said, did Marie go to see him? Still no questions. She must have forgotten again, I must call. He said that, he said he was going to call on the plumber. And I didn't say another word, I know why, now. Because while he was still dozing I had been imagining him waking up and tellng me that he had some things to do, adopting either an absentminded or a mysterious air, which comes to the same thing, and me being intrigued and asking him

what they were, and him saying I'll tell you later, and me knowing that
he wouldn't tell me, he knew I would have forgotten, so he'd evade it by
a circumlocution and I should be hurt, I'd tell myself he's treating me as
a nobody, and I knew I would get so furious with him it would drive me
crazy—I'd imagine him trampling all over me as he was putting on his
beret a few moments later and I'd be totally bereft. That's why I didn't
say anything. Because I may well be foolish but I'm not stupid. I don't
want to be everlastingly falling into the trap. I do after all have my own
life, I have feelings to be considered, I can't go asking for wounds and
affronts, I've had my bellyful of affronts, that's what I most need to
avoid. When I was young I believed, always with that mania for trying
to improve myself, that affronts, wounds to my amour-propre, were
good, they helped me to make progress. And I kowtowed, let people
walk all over me, with this in mind. Well, I realized later that this was
idiotic, very bad indeed, that I oughtn't to, or in any case not any more.
It made me lose all sense of myself, I had become a nonentity through
letting my amour-propre be felled, and it wasn't only me, and here was
the rub, it wasn't only me who suffered from it but the others too, quite
so, the others too. I could no longer even talk to them, I was all the time
afraid of thinking that they were thinking that I took myself for someone, so whenever I did say anything it was so muddled that they
couldn't understand a word, not only did they not understand a word
but they told themselves that I really was the all-time prize idiot, the
very first and foremost, they could absolutely not rely on me as they had
expected, as they needed to, they had expected to be able to cry on my
shoulder and all they encountered there was the stink coming from my
armpits, I was worse than useless, I was positively noxious. That's why
I don't want any more wounds to my amour-propre, that is precisely
why. Or more or less.

Or could it be the opposite? Do I still believe in what I believed in
when I was young? That's enough, that's enough. A little restraint.

When Gaston had gone out I went into the garden to see what
Fonfon was doing. I'd been thinking ever since the dessert that he must
be getting up to some sort of mischief or that he was climbing the
chestnut tree. I looked in the tree, I couldn't see anything. I went to the
shed, nothing there either. I went to the gate and looked into the street,
nothing. The afternoon was starting badly. I wouldn't even have that to
take my mind off things, no Fonfon to interrupt me. I haven't said this
yet but it's true, I'm always looking for something, if I'm not working,

but even my botany fatigues me and I'm glad to be interrupted. Looking for something or working, it comes to the same thing in the end, I'm saying it now, very quickly, to my shame, I don't often admit it, I hope I won't say it again. I also have to force myself with my botany. So having to look for something takes my mind off it, when I tell myself that I must find something first it's almost a little bit on purpose. But it fatigues me right away, it doesn't take my mind off it sufficiently, it's too much like looking for something else, and I rely on these interruptions but I still don't dare provoke them. In theory they happen of their own accord, especially Fonfon, the thought that I shall have to intervene. And I say to myself, one more interruption, I'll have to leave my work table again, what a bore, but I'm pleased. Yes, I'm saying it very quickly now, it might well falsify the whole of my exposé, it might well cause me a lot of aggravation very soon, I shall have to forget about it. And on the subject of provoking interruptions, even if I still don't dare to do so fairly and squarely, I may perhaps already have got into the habit of attracting them, of leaving the door open for them. This is logical because I'm always waiting for them the way the Good Lord is waiting for good souls. In the fog of the boredom of my botany or my ferretings I'm hoping to find the clear patches of these aggravations, I make my way over to the place where they're likely to appear, all right, it's my unconscious that makes the journey, but I'm the one who gets the benefit. I only have to say God how it bores me to go back to my magnifying glass for this pistil, or God how it bores me to go down this corridor for the millionth time to find that paper or that thing, I only have to say it a little too loudly or a little too softly and it awakens my unconscious which will then start on its little journey, it will very gently take me by the hand and lead me over to the clear patch. How it does it I don't want to know, my life would become impossible, I should never have any more aggravations. I shall never dare provoke them deliberately, I know myself.

No one in the street. Horrible light on the neighbour's house. My queasiness hadn't disappeared with the coffee, as I've already said, it was getting worse. I told myself that I ought to have something, a little brandy, a little marc, something. I went back into the refectory. I opened the sideboard. I poured myself a little glass of marc. At this moment Marie came in with her dishes. She noticed, even though I was holding my little glass in the hollow of my hand, making it into a shell. She said that's right, get yourself a skinfull, carry on, that helps matters a lot, doesn't it, that's a great help. She didn't sound spiteful, as she might well have, after our rows about the napkin and the butcher. This broke my heart. I said Marie I'm sorry about that napkin, I had completely forgotten that my handkerchief was in the craproom and you know how it is with Monsieur Gaston, if Fonfon starts sniffing he has to have his nose blown right away, had he already started sniffing, I can't tell you but he was going to, he was certainly going to, so you see I was in a terrible hurry, I took that napkin out of the drawer even though I knew I shouldn't, please forgive me, here, I'll put it with the dirty linen at once, and I went and got it from the corner. She said don't bother, I'll do it myself, give it to me. She still sounded quite pleasant. So I had to say something else even though I knew I'd end up irritating her but I couldn't help it. I knew I was going too far but I couldn't help it, and anyway I enjoy that, so I went ahead. I said you know about the butcher you were absolutely right, Madame Apostolos always says that a lady has told her but she mixes one year up with another, you know her, and if Gaston insisted he didn't mean any harm, or rather he didn't mean anything at all, he was irritated at not being able to find the grain, that was all. But I know very well that it's quite impossible for us to get anything better from the other butcher, my goodness, how well I remember that piece you couldn't even eat, I can still see you coming back with the salad and telling us that you would change butchers. She went on putting the dishes away in the sideboard as if she hadn't heard me, she's used to it. This shocked me a little. I wanted to mark the occasion. I said look, have a little glass with me, that always helps, as you say. She turned around and gave me such a stupefied look that it re-broke the other half and with the quarter of my heart that remained to me I poured her out a little glass. Nevertheless she didn't say no. I said sit down and let's talk about your niece. She didn't say no, and she sat down in Apostolos's chair.

Say later on what we said to each other.

We talked awhile, and poured ourselves out another little glass. Reber must have woken up in the craproom and been intrigued at hearing us. She came into the refectory, I can still see her opening the door and saying did I leave a needle in here by any chance. She saw the glasses on the table. She looked so stupefied that the quarters of my heart got stuck together again and I couldn't help it, I knew I was going too far, I made a nasty crack. I said well yes you see, *we* don't have recourse to the rosary, we have recourse to the bottle. I was going too far but it was because of the drink. Marie looked embarrassed and stood up, saying that she hadn't finished her saucepans. Reber waited until she had gone and then told me that my jokes were a sin, they'd recoil on me one day, you'll see, I wouldn't like to be in your place. I said neither would I. That might mean either in mine or in hers. She pretended to be looking for her needle and saw the napkin Marie had left on Apostolos's chair. She said you would do well to put it with the soiled linen yourself, as you said. And she left the room.

I'm trying to find a piece of furniture to make a break, I can't see which one.

And above all, I now realize that there's no longer any point in looking for my paper. I'm rewriting my life, I'm writing another exposé like the others, which is what I didn't want to do, I've let myself get carried away, it's too late to go back on what I've already said, I accept it. Nor is there any point in saying that all this happened today, it's a matter of sublime indifference to me. Whether it was today or yesterday or any other day it's the same thing to me and it will still be the same tomorrow, of no importance, of not the slightest importance. I'm once again starting to expose my life so as to try to get rid of it but I'm well aware that it's pointless. I don't have to ask myself why and I carry on, it gives me something to do. But something tells me that if I say that I'm no longer looking for that paper and that it didn't happen today this exposé will be even more of a flop than the others. I might possibly find out why if I tried, if I asked myself questions, but that gives me a pain in the ass, I'd rather not ask, just rely on my impressions. What I'm saying here, I'm saying it even more quickly for that precise reason. I don't want to have a worse flop, I want to stay on the same level. And so I say once again that I'm looking for the paper I didn't find this morning, I'm still pretending that I'm looking for it. Just the very word pretending has already put the kibosh on everything, that's why I shan't say it again. Quick, quick, forget. Fortunately, that's easy. Repeat, I'm looking for that paper. Repeat, I don't give a single damn. How simple that is. But it's so true, I give so few damns that anyone who could delve into the recesses of my mind would be astonished. It's a complete vacuum but it has been like that for so long that it doesn't bother me any more. Even the fact of knowing that I shall go on starting to expose my life is a matter of complete indifference to me. Some people might perhaps understand that but most wouldn't, and I repeat that I don't give a damn. That's what's so beautiful in one sense, for the people who might understand me, if there are any, and I don't give a damn, that someone *can* give so very, very few damns. This is perhaps the one thing that isn't really nauseating. To think that after all there is nothing that isn't of complete indifference to one. Neither having the runs nor being a failure all along the line. And that you can go on repeating it without wanting to vomit. It's even of incomparable beauty. Impossible to find anything to compare it with because we don't give a damn about logic. A little moment of pleasure to be savoured, and I *am* savouring it. That's it, it's gone. I'm not getting any more pleasure out of it. It's over. Repeat, I'm looking for that paper. That's what will save me. As usual. I mean that it may seem odd to think that one is saved because one has to start again every time not giving any damns about having flopped.

I got up at eight, having been woken by Marie. She knocks on my door three times. If I don't grunt she knocks again until I do grunt. Impossible to talk in the morning. Even yes irritates me. Especially yes. This morning I woke up at once, at least I think I did, I'm not sure. Must ask Marie. And I put on my dressing gown and went down to drink my tea in the refectory.

While I think about it, I know I'm looking for something but I can't remember what. I'm used to it. If it isn't that paper it's something else, it's of no importance. I shall say that paper, to simplify matters. One must always simplify, in order not to become complicated. One of the things I've learned and which is useful on occasions. But don't go thinking that I'm not looking for anything any more, that wouldn't be true and it would distress me. One of the things I am *not* indifferent to is when people do me an injustice. That may be why I still have some resilience.

I went down to drink my tea in the refectory. But I'd passed Apostolos on her way back from the bog. With her packet in her bulging pocket. As I went downstairs I was wondering whether I had actually seen her face on or if I was confusing it with yesterday, but I must have told myself that it was of no importance.

Another thing. If I say that it's perhaps not that paper I'm looking for but another it's for the following reason. I've just tried to redraft my botanical paragraph and I managed it very well, I had all the necessary information. I shall continue tomorrow. I'll finish this exposé first. And go on saying that paper though it must certainly have been another, equally indispensable in any case, you can reassure yourselves about that, equally indispensable. *I* am reassured.

While I was drinking my tea I made myself laugh by telling myself that it may have been Marie I passed in the corridor and that she'd said don't think it's me, it's Madame Apostolos, and that she'd aped Apostolos limping back to her room, her apron pocket stuffed with bog paper. Yes, that made me laugh, I'm not hard to please. And while I was laughing Marie came in to put something away in the sideboard and said why are you laughing, have I grown horns? Apostolos was there. She said she was feeling seedy, she finished her coffee and went upstairs to lie down until midday. That's it. I know where she was all morning. Simply, I didn't meet her in the corridor, slight correction. She was the one who asked me have I grown horns?

Shit.

But I'm beginning to feel like vomiting again. Just the very thought that I shall have to start all over again shatters me. I began too far back. I shouldn't have started again at all. Nor said certain things. I must go on. We've got to the afternoon. It's the gloom it plunges me back into that made me go wrong. I've unpacked my bag and I'm kicking myself for having done so. Let's forget it. I'll go on.

Just one little detail. It does sometimes happen that Apostolos comes down before ten and that was precisely the case this morning. She'd slept badly, she came down to drink her coffee to try to buck herself up but it didn't work, she realized that she was feeling seedy and she decided to go and lie down until midday. That was it, we won't mention it any more.

Reber went out of the refectory. I took the little glasses to the kitchen. Marie said she didn't want Mademoiselle Reber to think she tippled, she knows the trouble I had with my husband and that I'm always saying that drink is a disgrace, now I'm really in a mess and all because of you. I told her not to worry, I would this very moment go and tell Mademoiselle Reber that I'd asked you to have a drop of marc with me to keep me company because I thought that all that business at lunch had upset you, and that's actually the truth, isn't it? She said yes it actually is but tell her that you insisted, she's so spiteful she could well throw it in my face one of these days. I said I promise you. Tell Reber Marie. I went back to the craproom where Apostolos was still asleep. I moved very quietly so as not to wake her and I looked to see how far down we'd have to move Eugénie so as to hide the patch. Twenty centimeters at the very most. I pulled the hulk away very gently, then I put the stepladder under Eugénie. Next I took the toolbox out of the cupboard and looked for a nail ad hoc. There wasn't one big enough. And just as I was leaving the room again to go to the shed Apostolos woke up. She asked me was I asleep? To put her at her ease I said oh not really. Gaston has just gone out and so has Mademoiselle Reber. She asked me what I was doing, I told her I was going to move Eugénie to hide the patch, I was going to the shed to see if I could find a nail that was big enough. She said why don't you use the one that's already there? There she surprised me, she was quite right, but I'm so used to bending the nails I pull out that I could see it already bent, even before I'd tried. So I tried. And it came out just like that. I knocked it in again twenty centimeters lower but it wasn't any better, there was a much darker strip above it, the paper underneath the picture had stayed cleaner. Even though Apostolos told me that it didn't show, since I know that with her eyesight nothing shows I wasn't satisfied. I did think that the strip would soon turn yellow but it still wasn't a success. After that I returned the stepladder to the bookshelves and pushed the hulk back.

When things aren't going too well, take advantage of it to repeat to myself some of the elementary things that I think when I'm not writing. Repeat, don't try to be funny and interesting at all costs, that may be what made my other exposés flop. The fact that I don't want to be boring is quite normal but even so I ought to opt for monotony rather than phony amusement. I must say things that are true and precise. If I let myself go I wander, I overdo things, and we end up in pure fantasy. That's bad, bad. My life is difficult and boring like everyone else's, I know I'll never get out of it, just trying to find something new isn't going to get me out of it, on the contrary. I have more chance of getting rid of it by saying what is. Temporarily rid of it. A statement of the obvious, however distressing, isn't necessarily boring, it shouldn't be. When you have as little talent as I have you have to limit yourself to this. People who have talent can exaggerate, even when they jump in at the deep end they land on their feet. What's called transposition, which is poetry. Poetry is not for me. I was very fond of it when I was young and I made the mistake of believing that it *was* for me as well. One of the distressing things about life is to see people confuse their tastes with their talents, this is one of life's torturing little mysteries. Men, for example, who have a taste for business, who admire business tycoons, they launch out into business and spend their whole lives trying to make ends meet, trying to pay their debts. So they are not businessmen and they'd have been much happier if they'd simply concentrated on the business of living, they'd have made a success of that instead of losing their money and their marbles and not leading any life at all. Or people like me who are equally inclined to confuse things and who launch out into exposés which have nothing to do with their lives, simply because they let themselves be carried away by their imagination. Repeat, everyone has imagination. Repeat, everyone wants to escape from his life. Repeat, my only chance of escaping mine is to stay in it conscientiously. When I talk to myself in this way I still have the impression that I'm exaggerating, that in trying to be funny I'm overstating the case by insisting on the boring side. But this too is an illusion. My desire to please is so pronounced that I'd take advantage of any situation to try to do so but the result is that I'm bound to fail every time. And this isn't *my* catastrophe, either. Up till now I have already greatly exaggerated in this direction, greatly, and I apologize. Fortunately I am lucid from time to time. But basically I'm only apologizing for it because I'm afraid of being a flop yet again. So what I still have left is the hope of being less of a flop this time, I said the same level but I was exaggerating, I do have the hope that his will be less of a flop, I must admit that. All this because for a time I believed that hope was a flaw. I thought it was a characteristic of flawed people. So as not to exaggerate, let's say of the weak, of people like you and me. But I didn't include myself in this job lot, oh no. It's pathetic to kid yourself to such an extent. So I wallowed in despair, that was my delight. Not only to kid yourself but to be so dishonest. Yes, I was dishonest. Serves me right that my exposés were a flop, I deserved it. In this one, the moment I find myself starting to stray from my path a little under the pretext of being more interesting than I really am, I must immediately find a way of spanking myself. If only I had someone! Someone who would read over my shoulder, but that would be too good to be true. You have to be responsible for yourself. Responsibility. Don't let's insist on it, that's not my department. If in order to be absolutely honest I have to say that we are responsible, well then I do say it, and the beginning of my exposé isn't true, I admit that with joy. Not joy. Submission. And I repudiate everything I have said up to now, I mean the paragraphs which don't ring true. I can never take enough precautions. This is what I'm going to do, it's just occurred to me. Every time there's a bit of a bad smell about it, that I sense some exaggeration, I shall stop, and imagine there's someone squinting over my shoulder. Then I really shall have to put the damper on, I really shall have to stick to the truth. Yes, that's a good scheme. I'm writing it down. On a piece of paper. There. And I'm putting it by my side. I shall leave it there on my table, I can see it all the time.

It hasn't been dark for a long time. The owl is snoozing. But I'm carrying on. The sun will once again be heating up the roofs and the garden, that ghastly light will be there all day long. At this moment I must say that it's less ugly although I don't want to fall for that particular hope, that would be too stupid since I know that it isn't one. Even so, mustn't see hope everywhere. There are a few swallows, yes. Fortunately they aren't twittering. I believe they only twitter at the start of the season, when they arrive. But I may be wrong. At all events, this morning they aren't twittering. I can see two or three over in the direction of the cathedral, not nearly so far as the cathedral, if they were that far I'd barely be able to recognize them. To the right of the Rivoires' house I can see the first houses in the street, which slopes downwards, and if I get up from my chair I can almost see, or rather imagine, a little gap, not a gap, a little difference in the light, which indicates that there's a hollow and that the river is flowing below. But that's because I know. Anyone who came up to my room for the first time wouldn't see a thing. The sky is pale, that fine-weather sky that makes me... My scheme is working. Remember scheme.

I'll take it up from where I'd got to, with Marie in the kitchen. I had promised her I'd tell Reber that it was my doing, that I had insisted. Tell Reber Marie. And I went out into the garden. I told myself that this wasn't the moment to speak to Reber, who had just got settled in the garden again, I hesitated maybe two seconds, three seconds, my queasiness still hadn't gone, I went back into the craproom. No, I'd got up to Eugénie. I've just moved her and I notice the darker strip above her and Apostolos tells me that it doesn't show. That was it. She looked all-in. Really seedy. I felt she would have liked me to say something mushy, something sad about life in general and about her past, her various exiles. That's the only thing that bucks her up. But she didn't like to ask me, she raised her eyes and then immediately lowered them. She was idly fiddling with one end of her triangular scarf. She often wears a scarf, she has heaps of them, flowered ones, almost all with flowers except one or two, two I think, let me remember now, maybe she has more, two which don't have flowers, one with stripes, another without anything, one white one. I can't say which one she was fiddling with, I don't remember. But I didn't feel up to plunging back into her life with her. I chose a middle course, I said why don't we look through Gaston's albums, what do you say? Without needing to make any transitions, to think up any phrases to lead up to that one. Right away she said yes. Which proved that I hadn't been mistaken. Gaston's album is in the top left-hand drawer of the chest of drawers. It's a photo album. Family photos. Guest house family. He used to take a lot of photos in the old days but not any more, or hardly ever, almost never. It used to be his pet hobby. Given the slightest opportunity, click, photo. This produced a whole heap of them which we stuck in the album, it used to be our evening entertainment. Actually, it was no worse than anything else.

I took the album out of the drawer and we sat down at the round table, that's better than having the album on your knees and I'm not keen on rubbing knees with Apostolos. The album nice and flat on the table.

Here I could describe all the photos without needing the album, I know them by heart. This will at least be one genuine moment, no way of cheating. First page, first photo at the top, me when Gaston and I had just re-met. I'm on the promenade along the park, on the sidewalk. It's summer. I'm wearing a dark short-sleeved sports shirt and white trousers, one hand in my pocket, the other in the air, I'm holding my cigarette. I almost remember having said to myself let's look natural, I quickly lit a cigarette and held it up in the air like that, as if he'd unexpectedly snapped me while I was smoking, and I was also trying to smile in a relaxed sort of way. Yes, I can say that I do remember it, or at least that I remember millions of similar occasions when I was telling myself let's look natural and carefree. I'd be surprised if I had actually been so carefree that time, I must have been pleased, I was pleased to have met Gaston again and to have talked things over and come up with the solution of the guest house, but from there to having an equally natural and equally carefree expression... I still have all my hair, I was starting to lose it and I was treating it with everything I could think of, lotions, massage, nothing did any good. I'm wearing white espadrilles. Later on I was against espadrilles, they stink. On the left there's a branch sticking out, with great big leaves. It was a catalpa and I told Gaston take it here, in front of the catalpa. Because I've always liked catalpas, it's a tree that makes you think of hot countries even though it grows perfectly well anywhere. On the left there's the road, just a bit of it. The sidewalk, then, is behind, and in the background, right against the park, a couple of females sitting on a bench with a baby carriage in front of them. They've noticed Gaston and they are looking in our direction. A little fox-terrier is trotting around the baby carriage. At the very back, in the extreme background a little to the right, the Savings Bank block with its dome and on its dome a flag flying. Above, a little fine-weather cloud.

Second photo underneath, still on the first page, Gaston in the same spot. Dark short-sleeved sports shirt, white trousers, espadrilles. But *he* isn't pretending to be relaxed. He's so natural that he looks almost stupid, he's wallowing in profound, mushy joy. He was so pleased with our project that the whole of his uncomplicated nature is as you might say oozing out of all his pores. He too is holding his cigarette in the air but he isn't pretending, he's stopped smoking for the photo. In the background, the females are still watching and the fox-terrier is peeing against one of the wheels of the baby carriage. I have a feeling, though I wouldn't swear to it, that from a distance, so as not to seem as if I was, I'd shouted out some witty remark to the females but I've forgotten what. It would surprise me if I hadn't said *something*, I know myself so well.

Third photo underneath, Gaston and me in the same spot. We'd asked a passer-by, a cyclist who was pushing his machine along the sidewalk. He'd put his bike down and taken us. In this one it's even more obvious that my smile is phony and Gaston's isn't. At least it's obvious to me. I almost remember too that I said to myself let's move closer to him, so it looks friendly, but not so friendly that it becomes ridiculous. And you can see that I've got closer to him at the top, from the waist up, but my feet are way over to the left so I'm practically losing my balance. It's horrible to know yourself as well as I do, you never get any more pleasure, you never have any surprises. The females aren't looking at us any more. The terrier is lying down by the baby carriage. A car is coming along the road towards us with its top down. Some way off. You can see the heads sticking out. In the background, still the Savings Bank and the flag flying. The little cloud is dispersing.

Next page, on the left, then, the cyclist. To thank him we'd said we'd take him with his machine, a new bike, he was terribly proud of it. He's a young fellow, white, or at any rate light-coloured short-sleeved sports shirt, dark trousers, white espadrilles. He has a broad grin on his face, even more natural if that's possible than Gaston, he's holding his bike which is glittering in the sun. Behind, the females are still not looking but the fox-terrier has got up, he's pulling on the leash. The car on the road has nearly passed us, you can see half the face of a girl who is raising an arm in our direction. In the background the Savings Bank and the flag flying. The little cloud is disintegrating.

Apostolos said how young you were, I mean to say it obviously makes a difference, you with your hair, and Monsieur Gaston so slim, what a lovely souvenir for you. I reminded her that people used to call Gaston the gentleman. She said he still is a gentleman, you know, he's a very cultivated man, that is a quality that lasts for ever. I said yes of course but physically what can you expect. She repeated very lovely souvenir, and the cyclist, you didn't know him? She really did want to have a wallow, considering how long she's known that we didn't know him. I said no, not at all. We'd promised him we'd send him his photo, he'd given us his address, and you see, there it is. She said what a pity, it would have been a lovely souvenir for him.

Right-hand page, holiday friends. People we'd met there. A man and a woman, she wearing a big hat and light-coloured dress, he with his raincoat over his arm. The faraway, lost look of holiday friends. What had we done together? What had we said to them? Can't possibly remember. They must have been nice if we took their photos. We certainly told each other that that would make us friends for later on, that we would invite each other to stay. They're in the park, in front of the bandstand. A child is perched on the balustrade.

Next photo, me on the beach with other holiday friends. We make a very carefree group, a boy is holding a bottle and a girl is drinking. The others are laughing. I look a bit less stiff than usual, I'm sitting cross-legged with a towel around my neck. A touch of the sun, no doubt.

Next photo, these same friends without me. They're at the end of the diving board, some sitting down, some standing up. Still those laughs. But that faraway, lost look, diving board or not, smile or not, they all have that look. As if they were still signalling to us not to forget them, as if they knew even then that it was hopeless.

And they go on like that over four pages, dating from the time when Gaston and I still used to go away on holiday together. How long did it last? Two years, the third year it was only a sort of half-holiday, we already had too many expenses. After that he went back to spending his holiday with his mother, after that every other year, after that less. On the fifth page it's the start of the guests. When we stuck in the photos we didn't put them in with us at first, even though they were already there, some of them, right from the start.

First of all Reber arriving with her taxi, she didn't come by bus. The taxi had driven into the garden and in its maneuvers it nearly ran over the aucubas, I can still hear Gaston yelling. He must have been taking photos of the garden, the smaller ones on the same page, he took advantage of this to photograph Reber and her taxi. I'd already taken her bags out and she'd already counted that there was one missing. Gaston took her like that, by her bags and the driver, they're both smiling. Behind them you can see the open gate and the neighbour's scarecrow but it isn't the same one, with a cap instead of a felt hat.

The next one is still Reber but not the same day, she's sitting in the garden, not yet on the red chair, she bought that later at the Magasins-Prix. Right from the start Gaston had told me that this lady was just the right sort, we would never have any trouble with her the way some people do with coarsely-spoken guests. He didn't know her yet. And physically, he thought she had class, that slender body as he said and that grey dress and her shawl hugging her shoulders and her hair scraped back, yes he was smitten with Reber and he'd taken another photo of her while she wasn't on her guard. You can see her lowering her head, she's put her work down on her knees, needlework, not knitting. And she's doing what I saw her do later and what she still does, she's reciting three aves between two false hems.

The next one is me, with my paint pots, on the steps. Not counting the smaller photos of the garden around Reber. You can see that the chestnut tree hasn't yet been truncated. But also that the shed is still totally dilapidated. As for the question of the neighbour's scarecrow's cap, I don't remember when he changed it. Maybe he's made a new scarecrow several times, in ten years. Details of that sort escape you. Unless it comes back to me later on.

The difficulty of remembering exactly the photos that follow, in their proper order. So what. One of the next ones is the arrival of the Cointets. I've already taken their bags upstairs, Madame Cointet has already counted that there was one missing. Gaston had kept them in the garden for a kind of honorary apéritif, call it what you like. A little glass of white wine under the arbour as he said, he liked to use phrases from songs. It was touching in one sense, he believed he was making his dream of life in the country come true and that we were going to drink white wine and twiddle our thumbs, something like that. You can see Madame Cointet, very gaunt, very pale, sitting up very stiffly on her chair, her hat on her head, her chemisette and a light coat that must have been beige, she wears almost nothing but beige, it looks English. She has a tremendously distinguished air but she's missed the little bird, she's darting a glance at her husband who is no doubt not saying the right thing or who has something wrong with him, his jacket maybe, you can see that it's unbuttoned. They're in front of the Rivoire wall, Gaston had pushed the little iron table over there to get more sun.

The next ones, the most interesting ones, are those of the picnics. Those ghastly picnics we used to organize at the beginning on Sundays, after the Cointets and Reber had been to Mass. They go to the ten o'clock Mass. The Cointets always go on their own. Reber has already left, she needs to meditate before the service. They often come back together, at around eleven thirty. So in the old days we used to organize picnics in the summer. This was at the beginning, we were discovering the countryside, new brooms sweep clean. And we used to go either down to the river or up into the hills, where it isn't yet too desolate. But all the photos of picnics, when I think back without really thinking, I mean to their first impression, I can only see them among the scrub, among the thorns, or under a dead tree. It must be psychological. Even though I see the grass when I look through the album, even though I know we are in the grass or in the undergrowth, when I think back all I can see is a bleak landscape. Madame Cointet is always at the apex of the pyramid, we always get together in a group to be photographed, her husband is usually on her left, she towers over him by a good head and a half, and Erard or even Apostolos are on her right. This is no doubt because most of the time she actually is at the apex or else because she holds herself so stiffly that in each photo you notice her before anyone else. When the thought of a photo of a picnic or let's say of a group comes back to me I shall take care that the first thing I do is get rid of the dead hills and describe it as it is.

When Apostolos and I got to the picnics she said our picnics, our lovely picnics. What a pity we didn't continue with them. Why didn't we continue with them? This idiotic question coming from a rheumaticky old woman who can no longer drag herself around wasn't actually so idiotic. The reason we gave them up was neither Apostolos's rheumatism nor the fatigue of one or other of the guests, physical factors, I mean. It was our morale, the awful bore of going for yet another picnic after so many previous ones, always to the same places, with those stinking oranges, those hard-boiled eggs, those sardines, the ants, the sun, the gradually increasing disgust with our community, we had nothing more to say to each other, after we'd gone into ecstasies over the hazel tree or the bracken, than what we said to each other around the table, so we might as well stay there. Yes, that question touched me. I replied you know I think that it actually put the maids to a lot of trouble, and Madame Sougneau didn't really enjoy the picnics so very much, don't you remember, it must have been that, it was certainly that. She fell into the trap. She said even so, it is exasperating to be the slave of the domestics, as she would have said in the old days, before her exiles, revelling in the word domestics. She was bucking up.

Another photo I remember is the one taken with a flash, one winter's evening, on the hulk in the craproom. In the center, Gaston, he looks very gentle and already a little shrunken, it's true that you do tend to sink back into the hulk and that Gaston's back is rather limp, he lets himself flop when he's sitting down, he would never dream of straightening himself up like old Cointet. I had thought that we could put her on his right and Apostolos on his left, we'd already tried that out but he didn't want it, he said no, our collaborators on either side of me, if the ladies don't mind, that would be nicer. We'd called the collaborators, who were in the kitchen, and they had posed beside him, Sougneau on his right and Marie on his left. There was still half a place on either side of the maids and I'd asked everyone to move up to the right a bit to make room for Apostolos on the left. She'd gone to stand there but it wasn't right, it looked too crowded with those three women and Gaston squashed in between them, and he was no longer in the middle. They moved again and we put Apostolos on a chair to the left and Madame Erard on a chair to the right. That filled it in widthwise, it was even a bit cramped, Apostolos had to lean over a bit towards Madame Sougneau, and in fact you can see that she's leaning over. I was a little upset that all the ladies weren't sitting down, especially Madame Cointet, but I was having trouble fitting the width into my lens and I let Madame Erard stay sitting down, Madame Cointet had insisted on that, I remember, saying our little Madame Erard is tired, you sit down there, I'll stand behind with the gentlemen. She may also have been influenced by the pyramid which they all had in their mind's eye, after all that time, and she found herself back at the apex with Perrin and Vérassou on her right, and her husband and Monsieur Erard on her left. Fonfon had to kneel in front of Gaston, he was already there, but the little bird had flown away to the left and he came out all fuzzy.

When Apostolos and I had finished looking through the album she

was all-in, me too. I can still see it closed on the table, I didn't feel like
going and putting it back in the chest of drawers. We waffled together
about the past, about the various arrivals. She well remembered the
arrival of the Erards, the last ones. We were having dinner, it was
winter, we weren't expecting anyone. I heard the gate creak and I went
to see. I switched on the outside light and saw a little woman in a
raincoat, her hair sticking to her head, she wasn't wearing a hat, it was
raining. And a man staggering under a couple of big suitcases. I immediately said come in, come in, they didn't want to, they were soaked
through. At first they wanted to stay in the corridor to tell me all about
it but that wouldn't have been very friendly. I hung up their raincoats on
the hat rack and showed them into the craproom, apologizing, we were
in the middle of dinner but that was of no importance. They apologized
too, they apologized, they didn't even dare come in with their dirty feet,
they stayed on the doorstep. I half-opened the refectory door and said to
Gaston here a minute, it's some customers. He said to the others you
carry on without us, Madame Sougneau will keep ours warm for us. We
pushed the couple into the craproom, they still didn't want to go in,
Madame Erard said at least let me take my shoes off and she did take
them off and she left them in the corridor, her stockings were soaking
wet too. I think Erard didn't take his off because he had holes in his
socks, the next few days she never stopped mending them. They went
on apologizing, that this was no time to arrive, especially in such
weather, but this is what had happened to them. And they explained
absolutely everything, from A to Z. They'd missed the eleven-twenty
bus and then waited until seven for a taxi which didn't come so they'd
decided to walk. It wasn't true that there weren't any taxis, they ought
to have realized that we knew that, there are always two at the station
that almost never get any trade. Furthermore, there was the evening
bus which had left at six-twenty. In short, when they arrived they had
seen our advertisement at the town hall. And they had thought it might
suit them. I wondered why they didn't walk here right away if they
didn't want to take a taxi but that was of no importance. We're used to
the explanations of the poor. They never dare tell the truth, it would be
so much simpler, but they always consider it a bit sordid, even when it
isn't, especially when it isn't. They imagine that it's unsavoury, as if they
were the only ones who had encountered it. They didn't dare say for
instance that Madame Erard had spent the whole afternoon looking for
a sewing-bee or some sort of market for her dolls and that they'd

re-missed the evening bus and had come on foot in spite of the rain. In short, they went on apologizing in all the wrong ways. We told them take it easy. Gaston signalled to me that he was prepared to have them while I was talking to them, and I did the same while he was talking to them. I went and fetched the firewater from the sideboard to warm them up and the others said who is it now, some more lame ducks? I said you'll see, at all events they're very genteel. The ladies like that. And I went back to the craproom to offer them the firewater. They made a great song and dance about accepting, so I quickly added that will be your apéritif, I don't suppose you've had dinner yet. Madame Erard had it on the tip of her tongue to say yes we have, I noticed that, but her husband was starving and said we just didn't have time, what with waiting for that taxi. I went to the kitchen to tell Madame Sougneau to make some more rice quickly and some fried eggs, something, you'll know what to do, you're so good at coping, I even had to flatter her. And I went back to the craproom where the Erards were coming out with their life story, the firewater was having the opposite effect, what I'd wanted, rather, was to get things moving, for us to agree on terms right away. Madame Erard had to tell us all about her husband's profession, and about how she did the odd job here and there to keep herself busy. To keep herself busy my foot. Even so Gaston did manage to say that we asked people to pay a month in advance. Erard said that would be fine, giving a little cough, yes that would be fine, that was all right with him. And we asked them to come in and have dinner, they would make the acquaintance of the others. They changed colour, poor things, as if we were going to introduce them to some duchesses. Madame Erard was ashamed of her plastered-down hair, she said I could eat in the kitchen, she ran a comb through her hair and hid her wet feet under her chair, curling back her toes. I said no, we're a family, you are one of the family, you mustn't stand on ceremony. And I laughed, took her arm, and led her into the refectory. She was quite flushed. The others had finished, they'd stayed at the table to indulge in their suppositions and gossip. I didn't even bother to look at their expressions when they saw our lame ducks, I quickly said let's drink to the health of our guests, to put them all at their ease. Things I did much better in the old days than I do now. There wasn't any more wine on the table, Vérassou went to fetch some from the kitchen and he came back with Marie and the rice. We called Sougneau in too, so she could make the acquaintance of the lady and gentleman right away. She had taken her apron off before she came in. But she judged the new arrivals immediately, which wasn't difficult though she made it rather obvious. Then the others went into the craproom and we ate with the couple. It was at this moment, rather, that they told us their life story. Of no importance. Everybody's life story. They had finally reached harbour, they could never have hoped to find it right away, and your house is so pretty, and those people so nice, it was Providence. We said no no, they said yes yes.

Apostolos told me just imagine, I can tell you now all right, just imagine, I believed at that moment that they were burglars, they they were telling us a trumped-up story and that they were going to rob us during the night, I locked my door as I always do but I also pushed my table against it and tied a string round the clasp on the shutters. But I think she'd already told us that. Or had I imagined that she had? Of nor importance. Actually, the more I describe our life the more pointless it seems for me to say exactly what happens, exactly what the guests say, to cudgel my brains to try to say it exactly, it's so uninteresting, so commonplace. Should I stop my exposé at once, then? No. I have invested a little hope in the personal remarks, I'm relying on them a little. Even a lot. I didn't go in for enough of them in my other lives, that may be one of the reasons why they were a washout. The idea occurred to me when I was working on my botany. Without really admitting it to myself, that's what I've been wanting for a long time, an exposé full of personal remarks, because they say, I've heard it said, that the more personal you are the more universal you are, and that encouraged me, it encouraged my unconscious, not me at that moment, I wouldn't have dared allow myself to be encouraged, to nourish this project. But now that I've got going, and that my unconscious has been left behind, I must admit that even if I *am* relying on things that are personal to me I still have the runs. If that's what universal is, well, shit. All the time telling myself also that they say, I've heard it said, that in actual fact there's nothing sensational about the universal, it's merely lived experience. But I would prefer to have heard amiss, I'd prefer the universal to be a little less of that, even if it meant re-messing up this exposé. For myself, I mean, for my personal satisfaction, not satisfaction, my I don't know what, I'd prefer that. And I can't shut my trap completely when I think about it because I'm not against hope. In short, you understand me.

Am I finally going to leave Apostolos? What else did we say? On the subject of the Erards, at all events, we only said one or two things, the wet hair for instance and the shoes and the burglars, it didn't last long, we spoke about other arrivals and about wet paint which smelled so good and about when they built the factory, all these are things I shall have to say later, mustn't get into the habit, it'll be total chaos, I shan't know where I am any more. When we'd finished bucking ourselves up with our sighs I said to Apostolos I must go, I have to look for that paper in the garden. And I went out. In the garden, Reber beckoned to me. *Now* what did she want of me. She said she didn't understand my attitude. Encouraging Fonfon's bad habits at lunch, as if I was sneering at them all, and then with the coffee sneering at her when I told her that the walls would still be more than she deserved, it's all the same to me you understand, it's not the first time, I know you, these fits come and go, it isn't spiteful, and even if it *was* spiteful, that's life, we have to put up with one another, in order to gain merit, she would never have enough to put up with in order to gain merit, in short, a regular string of vulgar abuse. And that it was therefore not for herself that she was telling me, it was for the others, so as not to fan the flames of our nasty little squabbles, it could push them to the limit, they might well not have the wisdom that she herself had acquired, they wouldn't turn it to advantage, but for me, for me, if I continued along those lines it would be far from salutary, and for Fonfon, what would I be making of the poor idiot? She didn't understand that I didn't understand, she asked me to think it over. She shifted her glasses, one purl one plain, she pushed them back, I ask you to think it over. I told her I would think about it but for the moment I had to find that paper, I couldn't carry on without it. She said since this morning and you still haven't found it? Have you looked in the garbage can? The garbage can. Hadn't thought. I thanked her and went to look in the garbage can which is in the left-hand corner when you're looking at the façade, a little recess between the street wall and the house, before you get to the craproom window. I retraced my steps and went to the shed to get a soap box to empty the garbage can into, I had to do things thoroughly. Then I emptied the garbage can, a revolting job, I re-saw everything we'd eaten for the last three days, how could I do that in this heat, the smell got me by the throat. All the peelings of the zucchini and the eggplants, the rotten parts of the tomatoes, the spat-out gristle of the steak, the scrapings from the sauce-pans, the stumps of the lettuces, the eggshells, the mouldy remains of the ratatouille, it's quite true that it doesn't keep, the bits of material from the craproom all mixed up with great balls of dust already impregnated with the grease from the plates, bits of paper stuck on to the bottom for God knows how long, the lot, I looked through the lot. Reber shouted you ought to wear gloves to do that. Gloves, gloves, I'd have to have some gloves, do I wear kid gloves? When the whole lot had been returned to the garbage can I went and put the soap box back in the shed. I told Reber I hadn't found it but that was the last time I'd let myself in for such a job, it's revolting. If she had told me she'd been praying for me all the while it wouldn't have surprised me. When I came out of the shed she said you ought to go out for a bit, that would take your mind off things, why don't you go to the wood, it must be pleasant. But I didn't feel like it and I went back to the refectory, I still hadn't looked in there. Marie was just going out. She said did you tell her about the little drink? I said not just now, it isn't the right moment, I'll tell her later. Tell Reber Marie. What else was it I had to remember? Eggplants? No. Canary. It's coming back to me. Say what? To Apostolos? It'll come back. Marie told me don't forget, I have to go out, but do let her know before this evening, please. She was very polite all of a sudden. I told her that's all right, you can rely on me. How stupid she is, poor Marie, as if she didn't know that I should forget. Her amour-propre is greater than her stupidity. Just like everyone else's. She told me she would call in at the plumber's, this time she really would remember, she would even do that before she went to the Magasins-Prix. Very polite all of a sudden, very submissive. She added is Madame Apostolos still in the craproom? If so I could just manage to do her room before I go out. I said I don't know, I'll go and see. Apostolos was still asleep, I woke her up by opening the door. She asked me was I asleep? I said oh not really...

Of no importance. The album only comes now, not before. But in that case what did I do before? Repeat, of no importance.

Of no importance.

And now I have to talk about the television, otherwise I'd forget.

It was one summer when Gaston was on holiday at his mother's. Marie and Sougneau were away too and Reber too, which was unusual in July. It was the first time that this had happened and it hasn't re-happened since. I was all alone in the guest house with Fonfon. We got on extremely well, he didn't ass around so much, the others must get on his nerves. He was the one who woke me at eight, he never once made a mistake, and we had breakfast together. Oh yes, that's a wonderful memory. I even found the July light less ugly, and I even didn't notice

the smell of burned fat so much. I can still see us having breakfast, me
buttering his bread for him at my leisure, I'd slept well, so had he, and I
could look out of the window without feeling queasy. This is the sort of
memory that remains with you. After that we went shopping and hung
around a bit, looking at courtyards, houses, trees. Our district isn't ugly,
there are things worth looking at everywhere, and I explained to Fonfon
what there was to be explained. And we didn't buy either eggplants or
zucchini. Other vegetables. And no peaches. Apricots or plums if there
were any, or even raspberries one day, I remember I bought some
raspberries. And no steak, escalope and slices of liver. That was the life,
and how. When we got back I'd do the cooking, or rather I got
everything ready for midday, it was still only ten o'clock, and I'd get on
with my botany as usual only I had moved down into the craproom,
that gave me a change of scenery. Fonfon lived in his usual way too,
running around here there and everywhere but goodness, what a difference! This was when I realized that it didn't do the slightest good to
scold him when he played the fool. He still did, naturally, but far less.
Just the very fact of explaining to him why he shouldn't do such things
was enough, he didn't do the same ones again. With the nests and the
chestnut tree, no, I didn't succeed, but with lots of other things I did.
And for me, just the very fact of knowing that I would be the only one
to take him to task, that gave me wings as you might say, I was very very
gentle. Yes, that was when I realized that the way to teach him was to
touch his heart. I promised myself that I would get the others to
understand that, when they came back, but you've seen the result. After
that I would cook our grub and we'd have lunch. One day he asked me
why the sideboard had that umbrella on top, I told him that it was an
ornament, a decoration, and that made him laugh until he nearly
chokĕd. And whether the dogs were real dogs. I said yes, dogs copied
from real dogs, real gun dogs. And in the afternoon he drew some gun
dogs which looked like barrels with a tongue. They all had an enormous
tongue, longer than their tails, because dogs are always thirsty. I think I
would have been able to look after idiots, or at any rate children, if my
life had gravitated in that direction. It doesn't bore me to repeat the same
things, you must know that by now, and I have the feeling that I'm
learning too, it makes me think. In short, we had lunch. After that we
quickly did the dishes to get rid of them. He only broke one plate which
I replaced the very next day and Gaston never found out. And after that,
usually, almost every day, we'd go down to the river or herborize

together. It was at this period that he used to pick campanulas for me. He chased butterflies with a butterfly net I'd made for him with a handle and a bit of wire and some tulle I'd taken from the ladies' cupboard in the craproom. That was the cause of quite a few fleas in my ear when they came back, it was the kind of tulle or I don't know what it's called that's supposed to be sewn on top of the skirts that went under the blouse of, I think, Mademoiselle Reber. She too makes her own dresses but she's probably only made one maybe three times in ten years. And Fonfon had started a butterfly collection, he stuck them on corks wth a few flies too, the prettiest ones. Just the very fact of thinking back to that period makes me go all sloppy, all mawkish. The whole day was spent like that, no fuss, and then we got our dinner and ate it in peace, one day we even had our dinner in the garden, he enjoyed that, he'd cleaned everything up, the table and two chairs, and I definitely didn't feel depressed either before or after sunset. And then, in the craproom, I would tell him stories, without getting bored. And one day, I don't know how it happened, I told him the story of the grandmother they sat down in front of the television. It was stupid, I don't know what had got into me. The daughter-in-law said to the grandmother, to get her out from under her feet while she did the housework, go and watch television. But the grandmother was gaga and the daughter-in-law sat her down in front of the set without turning it on, it was all the same. And in the end, when she was even more gaga, she put her in another corner, not in the salon, facing the wall with nothing in front of her and told her, watch television, and the grandmother watched and left her in peace. And this story made Fonfon laugh so much, I couldn't get over it, he understood difficult things, I wasn't sorry I'd told him. Until the next day when he wanted a television, a real one. He'd remembered the part he shouldn't have. I tried to get him to understand that it was impossible, much too expensive, that I couldn't. This made him cry. The next day or rather that night I thought why shouldn't I hire one for a month with my savings, it might amuse me too, who knows. And the next day when we went shopping we chose a set on hire from the dealer and he came and installed it for us the same afternoon. Right away Fonfon wanted me to switch it on, I had to explain that there was nothing on in the afternoons, it would be this evening. And in the evening, I shall remember this for the rest of my life. When we switched it on and there was a serial, Captain Corcoran! Yes, for the rest of my life. I can't even describe it exactly any more, it moves me so deeply. Fonfon's eyes were bulging, he clapped his hands, he was unrecognizable. I thanked heaven for having given me the idea. Maybe I was going to be able to save Fonfon that way, with the television. But I was saving myself too, I might perhaps have been able to save myself. We spoke of nothing other than Captain Corcoran, we spent the whole day imagining what he was going to do that evening after dinner. Fonfon would switch the set on beforehand and I had to explain to him that the captain hadn't eaten yet, neither had we, we had to wait. And what didn't he wolf down then, I swear he didn't jib, he would even have wolfed down eggplants. And after that it was spectacle, amazement, paradise. Corcoran saved the princess, she was in love with him, he set fire to towns, he went horse riding in the bush, he took command of armies, and there was that tamed tiger, everything, everything, we held our breath, we were the captain's friends, we bandaged his wounds, we advised him to go back to the palace where his fiancée was waiting for him and he did go back there, he got married, he went off again to defend the poor, he conquered all the empires. And for a whole month it was like that, we *were* the television, on our walks we saw coconut palms everywhere, sunsets over minarets, perfumed nights, ships filled with cushions, and we departed for the tropics. Fonfon remembered from one time to the next, I didn't, in the end he was the one who was telling me. We came back to life.

And then one evening when we were sitting in front of the set, Gaston arrived. He was a day early. We didn't even hear him come through the gate, all of a sudden he opened the craproom door and saw us. He said what's all this, my word, you're mad. I explained that I'd hired it for a month, until tomorrow, with my savings, he needn't worry, order would be restored, the month is up now. But he was already thinking about his washing machine and he said you'd have done better to keep your savings for that. I didn't even dare tell him to come and watch Corcoran with us for the last time, he must be tired, I went and fried him some eggs in the kitchen, he ate them in the refectory and then went to bed. When I got back to the craproom it was over. Corcoran was over.

The next day the chap came and took the set away.

And that evening Fonfon still couldn't believe it, I had to explain that he must be reasonable, we'd had a wonderful holiday, we'd do it again next year. He began to sob. I finally told him that I'd see, maybe I would get our TV back in a few days, we'll see, yes yes it's even certain,

I'll certainly get it back from the store, but for tonight go to bed, I'll come up with you and tell you the next episode. And I went up to his room with him, he got into bed. I said wait a moment, I have an idea. I went to the shed and fetched the soap box, took it up to his room and put it down at the end of his bed. And I told him the next episode, in front of the soap box, making a great effort, all the time telling him look, look, the captain, or the tiger at the princess's feet, or the soldiers setting fire to the citadel. And he looked, he looked, and he saw, and he clapped his hands. We were like the grandmother. We were still with our friend the captain, we would never leave him, we had won.

And every evening I went up to his room to tell him the next episode, and every evening he got all red in the face, he clapped his hands. But I gradually made it less frequent, I only went up one evening out of two, then once a week, and then not at all. We had forgotten. Life went on as before with the guests, the slaps, the evenings that destroyed you. We had nearly been saved.

Where are you, my Corcoran.

After that what did I do?

Because the day isn't over yet, what did I do after Apostolos or after I don't know what?

I can't concentrate any longer. I want to die.

It's disintegrating. My exposé is disintegrating. All I feel now is my heart-ache which makes me want to give up the ghost. It's going to be like the other times, I'm going to have to start all over again later. I've messed it up once more. That this should come upon me like that all of a sudden—I hadn't foreseen that. It isn't normal. Try to explain it to myself? To take a hair of the dog that bit me? I was trying too hard to be truthful, I plunged too deeply into our life, I wanted to do too much, too conscientiously, and the net result is that death has come on the scene. I can see it all the time. I have its photo above my table, I didn't know it was death, but I can see it now, it *is*, it's looking at me and winking. It came into my exposé without saying a word, very quietly, to deal me that knockout blow with my Corcoran. I was trying too hard to say exactly what happened, I'd let myself be completely carried away by my holiday, my heart wasn't up to the journey, but what's the use of knowing? I don't know. I shall never know what use it is. Maybe I've been thinking back to things that happened too long ago? The longer the journey, the less the heart can hold out? Yes, that's it. But I've known that too for a long time. Then why, why?

Courage. I must carry on. All my wits. Carry on with the day without thinking about the others, the old ones, the pleasant ones. Plunge back into today's day which merely nauseates me, makes me want to vomit, but not to die. Plunge myself back into this nausea to be able to carry on, that's all I can do. Not try to get out of it any more.

I took down the photo of death, I put it at the bottom of my wardrobe, under the shoes.

What did I do after Apostolos. It's coming back to me. Marie went out with her hat on her head, I saw her going out of the gate. I was in the refectory, let's not ask ourselves how. I was looking for my paper, I thought I ought to look in the sideboard, it could have got stuck on to a bottle or a plate, these things do happen. I looked under the bottle of nine degrees. Tell Gaston wine. And under the bottle of marc. And under the old empty liqueur bottles. There was one which still had a little in the bottom, I opened it, I smelled it, it didn't smell of anything any more. After that I took the plates off the piles one by one and put them on the table, I emptied the whole sideboard and the whole cupboard with the exception of the top shelf, the Hermes statuettes. I was thinking of what I would have said to Gaston if he'd wanted to have the place repainted, I didn't want to empty that one to avoid making a shambles, it was quite bad enough as it was with everything that had to be put back. Reber was wondering what the hell I thought I might be getting up to, she came to the window. *Now* what are you doing, it's not possible, you're going to break everything. She came and helped me put the crockery back in the sideboard and the table linen in the cupboard. While we were putting the tablecloths back Apostolos turned up, she said are we expecting someone to dinner? I said no, who do you imagine we might be expecting, if at least we were expecting someone, no I'm still looking for my paper, things have to be done thoroughly. She said she would have liked to help us but she definitely felt seedy, she was going upstairs to lie down until the evening, would someone wake her when it was dinnertime. These old people who think of nothing but filling their bellies, are they laying in their provisions for the beyond? A reflex? I hope I don't come to that when I'm her age but that I'll quietly feed myself on yogurt and little biscuits until the hour of the tomb. It's true, just the very thought of those worms making pigs of themselves on my full stomach and my fat buttocks depresses me, and anyway I think it highly unseemly. A respectable thinness, which dries up quickly, no pulp at the bottom of the hole. Or better still, a thinness that dries in a little tomb with drawers, in the open air, like in southern countries near the sea. In short, thinness in any case. That's the very least we owe ourselves. These days there's that wonderful disease called cancer which makes old people lose weight very quickly out of simple decency in the face of death, but what do they do but start fighting against it, the terminal cases try to put on weight up to the very last minute. It's hardly believable. You can't tell me I'm inventing it. When people think the way I do but aren't sure of catching cancer as they go along, they should make the necessary arrangements in good time. I don't eat all that much, as it is, no one can say that I make a pig of myself, I'm always feeling queasy, but I shall have to cut down even more. As from what age? Sixty? We'll see. Remember thinness.

When we'd finished putting it all away, Reber said I ought to have taken advantage of it to set the table, that would have saved Marie the trouble. Their connivance crossed my mind again but only as a matter of form, I didn't believe in it any more. And she took some of the dishes back out of the sideboard and set the table. To start with she didn't find the oilcloth in its usual place, rolled around a broomstick in the corner by the sideboard, one of Gaston's ideas which he gets from his mother who can't bear oilcloths on dining tables after meals. Every day Marie has to unroll it and put it back on the table. In short Reber couldn't find it, she went to look in the kitchen where the oilcloth was stretched out over the backs of two chairs, Marie had... Cut the boring household details. I wonder what will be left. If there isn't anything left it will be over more quickly. Repeat, I'm going to carry on. It will soon be dinner time, thank heaven. After that there'll only be the evening and we'll have done the trick. The dirty trick. She set the table and I went into the garden. The light was becoming less ghastly, the afternoon was dying, I was going to feel better. I put the green chair down near the gate and told myself that I was going to daydream about the neighbour a bit, I remembered that morning's interlude with some pleasure, I was going to try to start again. I wondered why thinking about the neighbour had that effect on me, it was the only moment of the day when I had forgotten that I felt like vomiting. I was almost beginning to realize that it was because all things considered I was getting away from our shittery, my spirit was getting away from our house, it was an escape and a good one, not into the past but into the little future, I was getting ready to develop this idea when Gaston came back. What are you doing there, as if he'd never seen me on a chair before. Without waiting for my answer he said I called on the plumber, he's going to come tomorrow. I said that Marie was supposed to be seeing him too, she'd promised me. On what condition? I've suddenly remembered. On condition that I told Reber about the firewater. It *was* a condition, I quite understood that. But I didn't say so to Gaston. He looked tired, he'd been running around all afternoon doing those things he was supposed to tell me about later but which he didn't tell me about. It was certainly to do with the washing machine, he knows that irritates me. I said to him, just an idea, an old idea that happened to come into my head, shall we have an apéritif in the craproom, Apostolos has gone up to her room. He looked at me as if I was suggesting I don't know what, something indecent, then his expression changed and he said if you like. This surprise, simply because it was an eternity since we'd had an apéritif together. We used to in the old days but not any longer, I drink my red wine by myself as I've said. My suggestion to him certainly meant that something was taking place in my innards. My unconscious knew that I would decide to write this exposé in my room in the evening and that I would ferret around in our past. But *I* didn't know it. I was most amazed to have had that idea but I liked it. We went into the craproom, then, and I poured out two glasses of nine degrees. But this had made such an impression on Gaston that he was quite moved and he said maybe we could buy some Pernod from time to time, what do you think? Some Pernod, good God! I almost wept. Our Pernods in the old days—all our youth came rushing back! And how, I said, and how I agree, it would be almost like a holiday, I'll buy a bottle tomorrow. Remember Pernod.

And one thing leading to another, while we were drinking our red wine without saying much I started thinking back to the invitations in the old days, to the toad-in-the-hole game, to the smelly girls. Yes, those were good days, no question about that. Yes, even so we did have some days of peace, some happy days. While I was telling myself that I was forgetting all the anguish racking me at that moment, I was inventing a previous little happiness for myself that was totally false, that had never existed. What I've just said isn't original, everyone knows it but that doesn't stop it being extraordinarily stupid. It's universal, therefore it's stupid. Here comes the universal, I've unearthed it in passing. I suddenly feel less queasy. If only it would last. Say universal things.

The apéritif with Gaston. Careful not to say just anything. I want to conclude right away with a global view, a kind of tour of the horizon which would block all that exists, that's only normal, it seems to be the function of the horizon. But it isn't true. Nothing is ever concluded in life, not even in one like ours. Just because we believe the horizon to be within our reach doesn't mean that it exists. This is a view that stems from what philosophers call the ideal or from fatigue, it comes to the same thing. There is no horizon, not anywhere. The apéritif with Gaston, I don't know how long it lasted, I could find out if I wanted to but it doesn't interest me. The most difficult thing is having to talk about it now, given my desire to reach a conclusion. And I mustn't think, either, about what I did afterwards because if I wanted to make it last for all eternity and not to have done anything afterwards I could. Not with talent, but with a professional conscience. And I know that everything I thought at that moment was unblocking the horizon at every second, to talk in the usual way, but there wasn't any horizon. Repeat, no horizon. It has some connection with my thing about the nauseating future, that's also an ideal viewpoint, at any given moment there is no future, what counts is what you are doing. But these kinds of thoughts are too difficult for me, I'm running the risk of mucking everything up. What's more, the truth is that I stopped for a while, I've lost the thread, I've forgotten what I was going to say. In one sense I regret that, but in another I tell myself that it's just as well. I'm always complaining about not having any memory but after all I wonder whether that isn't what saves me. Saves me from what. From not being dead.

I'll leave until later the interesting things I wanted to say about the apéro with Gaston, which could if I liked become eternal. I'm sure there's something true there that's slipping through my fingers. Or do I think that because apéros are what I like best in all the world. Must mistrust my tastes. And besides, I've already simplified things a lot, my furtive glass of red all by myself is just so sad. But it reminds me of the ones before, which were what I liked best in all the world. Idiotic expression. Which I liked very much. And have I actually had so many as all that in agreeable company, now I come to think of it. Hasn't this only happened to me maybe let's say about fifty times, when I was young, and all the other times wasn't I trying to recapture the atmosphere and failing. And isn't this thing I say I like best in all the world merely an example of the sort of crap I believe is dear to me but which maybe never existed, let's say ten times out of the fifty or even, without trying to be funny, once out of the ten. One extraordinary time when an apéro marked me for life. What was it. When was it. I must have been very young, I must have thought that an apéro could never be anything other than white vermouth with salted almonds and it may even be that that particular time there weren't any almonds and someone said if you only knew what it's like with almonds. So even that time it wouldn't have been the ideal apéro, I would never have known it. Even so, let's not relapse into total imbecility.

A few more photos. They are the whole of our life. They are all we have left of it, I don't know what became of all the rest.

The Christmas photo.

In the center you can see Gaston slightly hunched up in the hulk, he's relaxing, looking comfortable and mellow, the same disarming nature, we'd had a little more to drink than usual, it was Christmas. The Cointets had been to the ten o'clock Mass with Reber, who had also been to Midnight Mass, she must have been pooped, all steeped in Masses like an old yesterday's salad, yes, I remember, I was expecting to see her come back exhausted with the Cointets at half past eleven, she was exhausted but she was smiling. All three brought their dream of persecuted babies back from the church, that meditation on the mystery of the Incarnate that simmers in the gravy of the turkey, stuffed with chestnuts and fondants, old memories, it's Christmas. I can still see Reber and Madame Cointet opening the door of the craproom, it was cold outside, they were all muffled up and the way they smiled at the sight of the tree which we had just lit up, with sparkling wires and garlands twisted all around it, covered in candles and little celluloid dolls and mandarins. The most beautiful tree they'd ever seen. Gaston and I bring out the old junk we keep in a shoe box from one year to the next. I had poured out the sparkling wine and we had toasted one another. After that at lunch we had had hors-d'oeuvres, Sougneau's Christmas specialty, tomatoes, eggs, anchovies, potato salad and olives. We count our olives and spit the stones out on to the edge of our plates. But no turkey. After lunch, coffee under the tree. Reber hums the Christmas carol about the divine child while we belch, each in his own corner. That year to enliven the afternoon I'd suggested a photo. We'd called the maids. We'd arranged ourselves. Our collaborators on either side of Gaston, Sougneau on his right, Marie on his left. Sougneau has taken off her apron, she's folded her hands over her stomach, she's looking at the lens as if she's watching the timer for the boiled eggs.

Fonfon has moved, and got in Marie's way, she's looking toward the left, which is the right of the photo. Next to her Madame Erard is showing us one of her dolls, to make things look cheerful. On the other side Vérassou, sitting on one buttock, is wearing his blue Sunday suit, or rather he's wearing the jacket, he takes it off on weekday evenings to save wear and tear. Next to him Apostolos on a chair, her head a little bent, a lost look in her eye, maybe she's thinking this is my last photo, no need of a chair on the side for the next one. Behind Vérassou, Perrin, Madame Cointet at the apex with her lace chemisette, her lorgnette hanging from a chain around her neck, this is her adornment for high days and holidays, it came down to her from her mother but she can't use it, not the same eyesight, she wears glasses when she plays patience. On her left her husband with between them a little celluloid doll all lopsided on the end of a branch, then Reber and Monsieur Erard above his wife, he has his right hand on her shoulder. When we were decorating the tree the day before, just to make a change Perrin wanted to put a little celluloid pig at the top, Reber was scandalized.

Or a photo of a picnic, in the center Gaston in his shirt-sleeves cutting the bread and the others around him sitting on the grass, slightly dishevelled. Madame Cointet has her parasol, her husband next to her is looking down at the ground, either he's lost his pince-nez or he's squashing an ant. Mademoiselle Reber is wearing a blouse, she'll have caught a cold by the evening, Sougneau would be telling her all the way home that you want to beware of the shade, you'll see. Marie on the outside of the group, a bit embarrassed, she's pretending to be busy, she's holding a plate. Vérassou is already eating his sardine, those ghastly picnic sardines which spoiled our enjoyment so much. Perrin is holding his fishing rod, while we're having our siesta he'll go wading and come back with a roach which we won't know where to put. Or else he brought it home and had Sougneau cook it, he ate it for dinner. The Erards. She's wearing a little summer dress, she's picked a bunch of flowers which she's holding up to the camera, he's showing Fonfon how you break hard-boiled eggs without breaking them and Fonfon is going to cry because his broke every time.

Or Reber would have kept her jacket on in the shade and taken it off in the sun and Sougneau would have told her beware of the sun, or else she'd left it behind and Sougneau said I don't understand, delicate as you are, why didn't you bring it, didn't I tell you. But Reber said that in weather like this it was a sin to bring a jacket, I've never known a summer to be so hot or so wait a moment though, yes, the year of my niece's first communion it was incredibly hot.

Fonfon had drunk all the lemonade, he got himself slapped by Reber, you can see that she's just lowered her hand and Fonfon is holding his cheek.

Or along the road, Apostolos limping and Vérassou carrying her coat.

Or in the undergrowth, Gaston going off with his handkerchief knotted over his head, he'll never come back.

Or the day when Cointet's sardine had given him indigestion, we'd made him lie down at the side of the road and Reber gave him some medicinal mint spirit on a lump of sugar.

Or that carcass in the dead hills.

Or someone.

Courage.

After the apéritif with Gaston I didn't feel like doing anything much, I'd have liked to stay there until dinner in half an hour but Fonfon wasn't back, I had to go and look for him. I went out into the garden again and asked Reber if she had seen him, she said no, but surely you aren't going to let that worry you. I went over to the gate and looked into the street. It's less horrible in the evening, the houses slope gently down to the river, you're almost sorry not to have been out all day and you don't remember that it was impossible because of the light. At the very bottom you can see the road curving around by the mechanic's, maybe Fonfon was there, he likes everything mechanical but especially grease, he'd come back in a disgusting state and Reber would make a scene. Or she would choke. I wondered whether I ought to go and fetch him but I abandoned the idea. What had to happen would happen. I sat down on the chair which was still by the gate and started daydreaming without even wondering what Reber was going to say to me. I'd had enough for that day. But I knew she wouldn't say anything, she too had had her bellyful. However much she says the rosary, that isn't much comfort or at least it doesn't make you feel like starting the day all over again. That's another thing I remember. I used to say the rosary a lot when I was young. Those never-ending decades and I realized that I wasn't concentrating, all of a sudden you notice that you're thinking that you haven't washed your behind, things like that, and you force yourself to think about the joyous mysteries, those pathetic stories in the catechism which are so beautiful and so difficult that you finally fall asleep. That may well be as good a way as any of getting to sleep but personally I've got out of the habit. Yes, I daydreamed and you know what about, about the neighbor. Because of the softer light I imagined that he was ill, we'd discovered by chance that he hadn't been out for a week and a neighbour came to tell me. Do you have a stimulant, anything of that sort, while we're waiting for the pharmacist, I've sent my husband to fetch him, that poor man is in such a state, if you saw how filthy his bedroom is. And I who had always imagined him living in a kind of cosy comfort, I was most surprised and I said to the neighbour I'll follow you, I'll go and fetch our marc. And I went and fetched the marc and I followed the neighbour to the neighbour's and we found him just as she had said in an indescribable hovel. Fortunately. His wretched bed in the middle of the room because of the damp wall, a blanket full of holes, a chamber pot full to the brim, bottles everywhere around the bed and a stove where there were the remains of some bacon. I went up to him and held out a glass of the firewater, he barely opened one eye, I poured the liquid down his gullet as best I could and he said thank you. Then you're feeling better. Much better, thank you. We didn't dare ask him what was the matter with him, we waited for the pharmacist. But what if the pharmacist wasn't there. Would the husband know what to do. Would he go and call the doctor. He lives a lot farther away. The neighbour finally said I'll leave you, I have some eggplants in the oven, I'll come back to see after dinner. And I stayed at the invalid's bedside telling myself that it could be me, what if it was me in a few years' time, abandoned, amongst my urine and my bacon. Not any sadder, actually, than not being abandoned. The neighbour had made his life like everyone else, he liked his freedom, why pity him for dying alone, probably drunk, I suddenly thought that he'd just finished one of the bottles, he didn't need my marc. And the day would end with his last breath, like in the splendid olden-day novels that we've never read. And perhaps after all this neighbour wrote novels. Why not. A recluse like him, what else could he do. Or his memoirs. After his death they found tons of manuscripts of the greatest interest. He was a man who had done everything, seen everything, an adventurer, a pioneer, an inventor. He had discovered a method for living happily on one's own but he explained in a postface that he hadn't had time to put it into practice for himself, he was bequeathing his discovery to posterity. The neighbour and I had discovered the manuscripts after the funeral and I told myself that it was my duty to read them, I'll give it as much time as it needs but it's my duty. And I had discovered what I've just said, that he had discovered that method. The first thing to do was to get in touch with a publisher, I asked Gaston what he thought about it. Gaston with his practical turn of mind said that I was getting ideas into my head, what's the point of getting all steamed up about that, and in any case the method can't be up to much, don't you see, he tried it out all his life and the postface is an author's trick, he didn't want to have failed, that was his way of redeeming himself in the eyes of posterity. And I discovered that this wretch, this down-and-out, this no-good, had an author's vanity, wasn't it laughable, when I remembered, years later, the hovel and the piss-pot. But I hadn't got that far yet, I was simply turning Gaston's words over in my mind and telling myself that he might well be right but that even so it was my duty to look for that publisher. And I went back to the moment when the neighbour was leaving me for her eggplants, I was wondering whether the husband would be back soon. And he came back with the pharmacist who said I told him so, I told him so. He didn't say what. Maybe he'd been taking sleeping pills and had poisoned himself. The pharmacist felt guilty for having sold them to him without a prescription. Or was it that the neighbour had gone in for botany and used to make himself herb teas out of whatever plant came to hand and that the pharmacist had warned him. That must have been it. This neighbour attracted me because he went in for botany, I didn't know it but my unconscious did. Such encounters do exist in life. That was why I wanted to get to know him, it was patently obvious. And I asked him a few days later but why didn't you tell me. He said what. That you were a botanist. But how could he tell me seeing that he didn't know that I was too. That's true though, how stupid I am, from now on, I told him, we'll go herborizing together, shall we. I didn't dare tell him that I'd discovered in his manuscripts after his death that his method was false, that I had read his method and that it was impossible to live on one's own happily. It was disturbing to be able to imagine no matter what and then to find yourself face to face with reality because all of a sudden he got up, went into his bedroom and came back with a pile of manuscripts. He said, here, read these, this is my method. A method, said I, a method for what. He replied for living on one's own happily, I haven't had time to put it into practice yet because I'm still writing it, I haven't quite finished, but it's infallible, you'll see. And a few months later he died without having had time and I told myself that it was my duty to try. I was thinking about that, I was touched by the idea of that method and that funeral, at the lawyer's office they discovered the will which made me a gift of the house and garden. This provided an annex for the guest house, we found some new guests, I was the manager of the annex, this transformed my life. Doesn't that unblock the horizon. It may well be that we go around in circles but even so, when you really concentrate, the horizon disappears. No horizon. Tell Gaston method. Wine, canary, method.

And Fonfon came back, I can still see him coming through the gate, I asked him whether he'd been to the mechanic's, he said no, I saw a duck on the river, I threw a stone at it to catch it. I told him you mustn't throw stones like that, do you think the duck likes it. He said he wasn't a duck. Reber shouted dinner's ready because she could hear Marie shout dinner's ready. We went into the refectory. We sat down. I said to Fonfon go and wash your hands. Reber said obviously it isn't by not washing them that he'll wash them. Marie brought in the remains of the eggplants. She said she had called at the plumber's but he wasn't in, she would go tomorrow. Gaston said he had called and he was going to come tomorrow. You called, when was that. I can't remember what Gaston said, what time, it must have been either before or after. Marie said this time he really will have to mend that leak, once and for all, and that she'd heated the eggplants with butter and parsley to freshen them up. Reber tasted them she said yes indeed, very good, I'll make them at my niece's. Marie couldn't manage to tear herself away, I can still see her, she was leaning against the door, she was bored in her kitchen. Gaston said well yes but even so all this pepper. Reber said these things must have some taste, pepper is very good for the digestion. I was seeing Gaston, who had got indigestion, lying at the side of the road, Reber was giving him the lump of sugar. He opened one eye and said that he had heard Sougneau perfectly well when she was telling Reber to bring her jacket, but it'll be like last time, pigheaded as she is she'll have caught a cold and heave-ho, the pharmacist to pay. I was opening the manuscript. An infallible method for living happily on one's own. Fonfon spilled some eggplant on his trousers, a great big dollop. Reber again said even so couldn't you take care, she was looking at me. Because I'd put Fonfon next to me again, she couldn't slap him. I told Fonfon go and wash your hands, they were covered in eggplant. Marie had gone back to the kitchen and we heard her hollering. I went to see. Fonfon had been trying to drink from the faucet, Marie had been trying to stop him and Fonfon had splashed her with the faucet swirl. It's a jointed metal swirl we put on the faucet to replace the rubber one which had perished. I brought Fonfon back with his shirt soaked through and Reber's fists were already clenched on the table. Let her choke for Christ's sake, and let her go and feed in the craproom. But she stayed. Apostolos was tucking into her eggplants saying that even so she preferred ratatouille, it's more tasty, you can't say it isn't. But Reber maintained the contrary, so as not to think about the idiot any more. She maintained, she maintained, she was quite prepared to say that she would eat nothing but eggplants from now on, that if she was on her own she would live on eggplants, the only method to be happy. But Fonfon wanted some more water, he held out his glass to her, she had assumed exclusive rights to the carafe. This time no and no, said she, and you won't go into the kitchen, I hope you are going to deal severely with him, she was looking at me. I said to Fonfon that's enough for the moment, we'll see when the dessert comes. He was going to cry. Gaston said let him have half a glass, these eggplants are too peppery, pass me the carafe will you please. That was it. She was going to choke but she wanted to stay. She passed the carafe and raised her arms to high heaven. And here, blow your nose, I said to Fonfon. Gaston said you left it on the chest of drawers. Fonfon came back saying the handkerchief wasn't there. Then Apostolos handed me hers, here, it was clean this morning. I blew Fonfon's nose and gave the handkerchief back to Apostolos who helped herself to some more eggplants. The rest of us had finished, we waited for her to finish. Marie shouted from the kitchen if everyone wanted fried eggs. Apostolos said she would prefer a boiled one, three minutes. Reber said I don't know if you're right, Marie isn't used to it she'll cook it either too much or not enough. Just to be a pain in the ass. She added, if we could spare her the trouble this evening, she's been running around all afternoon. Apostolos said all right and Reber shouted fried for everyone. What's all that she's been doing, what's all that she's been running around for, Apostolos wanted to know. It seemed that she'd spent the whole afternoon looking for shoes with straps that were cheaper than the ones in the Magasins-Prix, she hadn't found any, she'd had to fall back on the ones in the Magasins-Prix. Cheaper, cheaper than at the Magasins-Prix, not possible, you remember my flowered dress, there was nothing cheaper. She was twisting around in front of the mirror and Gaston was saying the hippopotamus while he was going through his bills. Marie was still glued to the door, she didn't want that machine, it was her or the machine, she was giving notice. Fonfon went out to pee. Did Reber finish her meal in the craproom. It wasn't fried eggs it was the remains of the steak but I just can't go on.

And peaches afterwards.

And coffee in the craproom

For years. Years of telling yourself that it can't go on any longer.

Try and keep calm for the coffee, the last one. By tomorrow's coffee my exposé will be finished and I shall already be regretting this one, I ought to have made it last. But nothing lasts. Night has fallen again, I can hear the owl again. It's stuffing itself with rats. It's a kind of Apostolos but with feathers and which doesn't need bog paper to wipe its ass. It deposits turds as big as eggs, the barn must be full of them, we sometimes find some in the garden. Back to caca. If only it could get moving again.

Or the photo of Apostolos's arrival one winter's evening, it was raining, she'd left her blue bag at the station, I told her you have it on your arm, she said she had telephoned, she'd got a wrong number, a lady had said what an idea disturbing people at this time of night, go to bed. She was crying. I said brace up, come in, you'd probably like something to eat. She didn't want anything, she wasn't hungry, she all but threw me out, she was referring to her niece, but that she'd telephoned. Sougneau had made her some fried eggs which she wolfed down saying all but, all but, what have I done with my little bag, I can't live without my little bag.

Or the one of the last picnic, the last sardine. Erard had got indigestion, he stayed in his room, Gaston discovered that they ate every other evening.

Or of me going downstairs at night to check the shutters, the door, the gas.

Where are you, my Corcoran.

It's disintegrating. Have I said enough in it. Do people realize. On the left as you come in, the craproom. Opposite, the refectory, which on the far side leads into the kitchen. The bottom of the staircase is in the middle of the left-hand wall of the corridor, after the craproom. When you get up to the first floor the Cointets' room is on your right with the Erards' room opposite it. To the left of the stairs first Vérassou, then Reber. Opposite is Apostolos. Then Perrin and the Erards. My room

and Gaston's are in the attic, also the maids', also Fonfon's. Opposite us
the Rivoires' house, the chestnut tree, the smell of burned fat, the light
that makes you want to throw up.

Keep calm. All my wits. There's no hurry. What did I do after the
meal. We went into the craproom for coffee. Gaston said ah you moved
Eugénie down, we'd have done better to leave her where she was, that
strip is frightful. I said it would disappear like everything else. I wondered
where my handkerchief had gone to, it wasn't on the chest of drawers.
Madame Erard began to take out her dolls, she only had one more to
make, she had worked it out, five dolls at five francs each which made
twenty-five minus the ten they owe us which makes fifteen, her husband told her don't bother your head, these gentlemen will understand,
isn't that right Monsieur Gaston. Reber said yes, poor little lady, she
must be very tired, such pretty dolls, wouldn't you like to stop for once
and play us that thing you know the one I mean, with the semiquavers.
Madame Erard got up, you mean the Trout, I'll be glad to, and she went
to the piano and drowned it. Madame Cointet said music my goodness,
nothing like it to go straight to the heart, it's like flowers and journeys,
and wham, the Borromeans. Apostolos asked for the sugar, I passed her
the bowl.

After that Mademoiselle Reber asked Madame Cointet when she
would be going on holiday. Madame Cointet replied on the sixteenth,
we've come to an arrangement with my niece, she can have us then and
it even suits her, just imagine, she's pregnant, she tires more quickly, I
shall be able to look after the children, I shall be delighted. Reber said
pregnant, doesn't she already have three. Four, Mademoiselle, she has
four, this will be the fifth. Reber said my goodness what a blessing,
what a lovely family, large families are a blessing, you will have five
great-nephews and nieces, I would like to be in your place, I only have
three, did you know that there were eight of us in our family, yes
Madame, we had a happy childhood, what beautiful memories, it's all
over now, the difficulties began with the inheritance, always these
money matters, I'm on bad terms with my sisters and the brothers, you
know what it's like, they're taken up with their wives and you never see
them any more. But I did everything I could at the time of the inheritance, everything I could to further my sisters' interests, though God
knows there wasn't very much, the family house and a few papers in the
bank, but they found a way to pick a quarrel and I'm still the one they
accuse, there's justice for you. Don't you think this coffee isn't hot

enough. Give me your cup, I'll go and heat it up in the kitchen. And she asked Apostolos, who was already snoozing, and the others. But there was only Madame Cointet. She took the two cups and went to the kitchen. Madame Erard had gone back to her dolls and Madame Cointet asked her whether she had studied the piano for a long time, she plays with such sensitivity. Madame Erard answered only for a few years with a teacher, after that I continued on my own and now, you see, I haven't time. But she darted a quick glance at her husband, she didn't want to hurt him, and she added I don't miss it at all, I like my dolls so much, that's just as much of an art as any other, look at this one, a little Breton girl, isn't she sweet with her little apron. Madame Cointet said yes, you're an artist. Reber came back with the two cups. Well then so you're leaving on the sixteenth. Five great-nephews and nieces what a blessing. And you Madame. Madame Erard replied on the twelfth, I promised my niece we'd spend the fourteenth with her. What a pity. Monsieur and Madame Erard won't be with us for the fourteenth, our beautiful fireworks display, it's so cheerful, it seems that the grand finale is going to be splendid this year, a lady told me that she had it from someone very high up in the town hall. Madame Erard said that she was sorry in one way but in another way not, her niece needed her, in any case they have a very nice fête too, we were there three years ago if you remember. Weren't we. She turned around to her husband but he was snoozing. Gaston too. And Monsieur Cointet too. Gentlemen are more apt to snooze than ladies. The only able-bodied person left was Vérassou and Reber asked him when he was going on holiday. He didn't know yet, he was expecting a letter from one day to the next, it would probably be around the fifteenth, his sister was having difficulties with his other sister who had had to move house, she had been staying with her in the meantime but she might well have found a flat before the fifteenth. This housing business, what a problem. And it's getting worse every day. Don't you remember in our day, everyone found somewhere to live, don't you think we're moving towards inflation. Reber says inflation for everything, it must mean revolution, perhaps war. Madame Cointet said don't say that Mademoiselle, two wars are enough, don't talk about it, it would be too horrible. So they talked about it, and made plans for the next one, they'd go to live with their nieces, in such cases you have to stick together, they knew something about that. Vérassou had gone up to work in his room and Perrin had gone fishing. I went out into the garden. Ghastly heat. One more

Sunday to kill, I would spend the whole afternoon looking for that paper so as not to get depressed. That's my own personal and private blessing, to forget and to lose my papers. If I had a good memory I wouldn't lose anything and then I wouldn't know what to do, I'd be bored rigid. Always having to ask yourself what have I forgotten, this keeps you going. And when you find something you'd forgotten to look for, what joy. This is very frequent. It gives me a chance to wonder when I lost it and whether I had told myself to find it, and when, and whether I'd made a note of it, and then I can look for the paper I may have made a note on, and if I can't find it I look for it and that gives me two or three good days. A bonus. So much stolen from the enemy. Who or what is my enemy. Time, which passes. I don't think so. It's more complicated. Psychological. Mustn't risk it.

I wondered where Fonfon had got to, he'd left the table at the dessert with his peach, I'd seen him making for the shed, he must have been ferreting around in his boxes. I went to the shed. He wasn't there. I took advantage of this to search the corners, my ball might have rolled into one of them, I could see Fonfon kicking it towards the chests. I moved all the chests and put them back again, and then I cleared a passage at the back, I saw Fonfon's nest boxes but I couldn't reach them. Ask him to show them to me. And on the right the gardening tools. Why do we keep them. We ought at least to clean them, to remove the rust. All this stuff, what a waste. In case we were to start planting things again. Touch-me-nots. And rake up the sunken gravel a bit, yes. I must do it myself, it's simple. Clean the tools and rake the garden. Clean everything, even, wash everything. Play the hose over the aucubas, over the wall, over the chestnut tree. Why not. They might perhaps be pleased to be able to sit in the garden. And tell the factory to put a gadget over the canteen chimney at least, or to keep the window shut and install a ventilation system to give them some air, it isn't normal, that smell, or that we should be stunk out to such an extent. Tell the local authorities. That's what we must do. Tell them we've been suffocating in our garden for years because of that canteen, is it normal, gentlemen, hygiene, public health, we shall get in touch with the minister, we have connections. They're frightened. They say but of course we shall do something and even right away. They go and see the manager of the factory who is obliged there and then to put gadgets over all the outlets or risk a fine, or legal proceedings, or bankruptcy. That's what we must do. Remember local authorities. Tell Gaston minister. We could spend some pleasant evenings in the garden around a lamp spreading a diffused light. Our flower beds full of balsams, our gravel crunching under our feet, our chairs repainted, and we'll get some armchairs too. Like in the beginning. And every morning I'll play the hose over everything. Immediately after my tea. There's a programme. We must carry it out. I've made up my mind Remember garden.

After that I went into the cellar and cleared the passage between the coal and the potatoes. That too was something I ought to do periodically. Not always rely on other people, on Fonfon who does everything wrong, on Marie who doesn't have time. And these daydreams in front of the hanged man's nail, what do they mean. Pull the nail out right away. Clean, do away with, get rid of. As I was coming out of the cellar Madame Cointet and Reber were going out for a walk. They were going to meet Perrin down by the river, it would make a nice walk for them. I asked them why the gentlemen weren't going with them. But they were still resting, they might join them later. You come with them, why don't you come too for once, you always used to come, do come, that will take your mind off things. They're always telling me to take my mind off things. Do they feel sorry for me. I don't care. I know what I have to do.

After that I wondered when Marie had come back from her shopping, I hadn't seen her. She was supposed to buy some cheese, there wouldn't be enough for this evening. I went to the kitchen to ask her whether she had remembered. She showed me everything she'd bought, some comté, some blue for Madame Cointet and Reber, some zucchini and tomatoes for the ratatouille, some steak, some butter, some rice, some eggs. She would make a risotto for this evening and a nice salad, the ladies like that. She hadn't finished doing her dishes, she said only a few more days thank goodness, all these people for just me it's too much, I can't wait for them to go. I asked her when *she* was going. She told me that she would really have liked to go before Madame Sougneau but that this year it suited Madame Sougneau better because of her niece. She would be going in August. She had absolutely nothing to wear, her dress was very shabby, tomorrow she would go and see what the Magasins-Prix had this year and if they aren't too expensive I'll buy a dress. Madame Sougneau had found a black silk dress in the sales, you really found much better things in the Magasins-Prix. I went into the craproom where the gentlemen were snoozing. Gaston asked me what I was looking for. I said Therese Neumann, I've been wanting to read it for ages. He said it's on the third shelf on the right. I took it out and put it on the table. Gaston said don't put it there, you'll only leave it lying about, take it right away. Erard woke up, he said where are the ladies. I said they'd gone for a walk down to the river, they've only just left, they wanted you and Monsieur Cointet to join them. Cointet woke up. He asked what we were saying. We told him. But he felt seedy, he had slight indigestion, he was going up to lie down. I said maybe the ratatouille, Marie puts too much oil in it as you may have noticed. But he thought it was the herrings, he can't digest them, I've known that for I don't know how long but I allow myself to be tempted. In fact his wife had told him not to have any, I remember that. You'll be ill again. But greed. He said that he couldn't take either herrings or sardines, those picnic sardines, do you remember. You can imagine how I remember, they spoilt all my enjoyment. You don't like them either. He got up and rummaged in a cupboard, he wanted to find an article to read upstairs. Madame Apostolos woke up. She said where are the ladies. We told her. She would very much like to have joined them but she hasn't been up to it for some time, she would spend the afternoon here, she'd embroider a tablecloth for her niece. She's been embroidering that tablecloth for months. Have I already said that. She added that it wouldn't be finished by August, she would finish it at her niece's. Madame Erard said I'll embroider a bit of it for you this evening, I shall have finished my doll. But Apostolos said she wouldn't hear of it, you have quite enough work as it is, you are too kind. Madame Erard told her husband to go for a walk too, she couldn't go. He said I won't go down to the river, there are too many people, I'll go round by the square, and he went out.

These Sundays at our place, these people who don't know what to do and who rehash their life story while they snooze. It must be the same everywhere. The Cointets and Reber are lucky enough to go to Mass, at least that occupies their morning. What was it they said at lunch that they'd seen when they came out. A lady, yes. A lady who had told them that she had changed her butcher, she didn't go to ours any more, he sells nothing but muck. And Apostolos told this to Marie when she came in with the ratatouille. Marie said she would never change back to the other butcher, one day he had palmed an uneatable bit off on her, she had had to leave it. Gaston said but since you've been told that he's changed, he isn't the same any more, might as well try, just have a look at this piece, he couldn't find the grain, I'm asking you to try the other one, but Marie had gone out banging the door. I told Gaston that she was probably right, you had to be prepared to pay for meat, the inexpensive cuts are always uneatable. But Reber maintained that the lady had told her that she bought the same sort of steak as we did and that it was much better at the other butcher's. I remarked that she probably bought a filet, obviously that's better. But it seems not. After that Marie came in again with the salad and I told her that she was right, the lady certainly bought a filet, that's why. She said obviously a filet, of course that's eatable, it's just what I thought. I signalled to Reber not to return to the attack and when Marie had gone out I said she's on edge today, there are a lot of people on Sundays, she isn't used to it. Monsieur Cointet said he understood, Monsieur Erard too. Vérassou said and anyway it's the same everywhere you know, I notice that the meat is always a bit tough at our canteen but it seems that this is very good for you, it makes you work your jaws. It certainly does make you work your jaws. Gaston still couldn't find the grain, in the end he hacked up the meat and we each had a chunk. They all got bits stuck in their teeth. To forestall the Borromeans I said you'll all be on holiday soon, that will give you something else to think about, and when Madame Sougneau comes back I'll ask her to speak to Marie, she's the one she takes most notice of, we'll try to go to the other one. Madame Erard talked about her dolls, she had five more to do before the holidays, then she spoke to her husband in a low voice, they were doing their sums, twenty-five minus ten minus five. We passed each other the salad. Perrin asked me if I wanted any and I was just going to answer when Fonfon started to stand up and knocked over the bottle of nine degrees. Gaston lost his temper, stupid idiot he said, can't you be more careful. Quick a hand-kerchief. I didn't have it. I told Fonfon go and look in the craproom. He came back saying it wasn't there. I wiped his nose with my napkin. Reber said you surely aren't going to wipe his nose with your napkin. But I really didn't care.

I must have made a mistake somewhere, we're back at lunch again, it isn't normal. Or at dinner. And before the departures. Of no importance. After the peaches we went into the craproom for coffee. Gaston saw Therese Neumann on the table and said what did I say, you leave everything lying about. He put her back in her place. Apostolos suggested a little game of bezique. I played with her while the others messed about. Vérassou went up to work in his room. Perrin rummaged in his cupboard for the Dreyfus affair. Cointet knocked over the little lamp while he was winding the wool. Madame Erard had taken out her dolls. The others were reading or saying they were going to bed.

One more night falling. I can't go on. This exposé has been a flop like the others but I'm used to it. I barely even regret it. I must finish it by saying what I did afterwards, when they'd gone upstairs. Gaston was in his armchair, he looked all in. I said only a few more days now, then we'll have some peace. He said yes, and start all over again in a month's time. I said why don't you take a holiday, that would take your mind off things. He told me that his mother wasn't very well, she'd written to him, his sister was going to look after her. And he went over to the catafalque to sort his bills.

Courage.

Feeling of having made more of a flop than usual. And above all of not having finished. I'm leaving behind a whole heap of undigested things, I haven't got rid of them. But how to retrieve them. Continue. It's by getting ahead that you go backwards more effectively. Personal remarks, still more personal remarks. This one for example. Hardship and depression notwithstanding I am let's say pleased about one thing. When I was working in an office I didn't present an accurate image of myself. That image will remain with the people who knew me at that time and I regret it. Forever hanging around in the streets and bistros, mixing with all sorts, not having any particular time to go to bed nor much in the way of morals. This isn't a false image, that isn't what I mean, since that kind of life was supposed to appeal to me. But incomplete, I think. The one I present now to our guests is incomplete too but fundamentally more truthful. Depressing, incomplete, but more truthful, in one sense. The disagreeable sense. Since we can't take them all at the same time. A simplified but more authentic image. I should like to be mistaken because I don't like this one either but I don't think I am.

Courage.

Gaston went over to the catafalque.

Or better still, since nothing is of any importance any more, go back to just before dinner. This wasn't the right one, there were only five of us at table. Precision and discipline.

The apéro with Gaston. He suggested that we should buy some Pernod again. Our youth coming back, correct. But I must have said a couple more words. Under the influence of the hogwash I must have thought about the future and seen it through rose-coloured spectacles and made some suggestions. That we should buy some Pernod again, yes, but that we should change something. That we should do more for our guests, we wouldn't be wasting our time. However much we complain about the education we received it has its comforting side. We know that what we do for other people benefits us. When this is the only solution all we have to do is get on with it, we'll find our reward sooner or later. As I said to Gaston, since we haven't managed to warm our hearts over all these years let's find something for our clients, if we saw them happy it might buck us up. He replied well well, you *are* making some discoveries, do you think I was born yesterday, my washing machine, then you don't understand. I'd goofed again. Filthy Pernod. He went over his sums again for me, five and a half months to be clear of the lot if we can manage to make the down payment. Or six and a half months. You can see that it's really nothing much, don't always be putting a spoke in the wheel. The future had gone back to its original colour and I went out to look for Fonfon.

Daydream about the neighbour. I went into it slap-bang, not making too many mistakes, probably, but not being very precise. Remember it exactly later on. It'll be too late, I know that. The exposé will be finished before. I've put off other things until later but which ones. With the same intention. The intention not to be able to.

Return of Fonfon. Story of the duck. Correct.

Reber bellyaches at table. Correct.

We sit down to table. Incorrect, there were only five of us. Me in my place, my back to the kitchen that is, Apostolos opposite me, Reber at the other end, Gaston opposite her and Fonfon next to me. Marie brought in the remains of the eggplants. She said she had heated them up with butter and parsley to freshen them up. She went out again. We helped ourselves. Gaston still found them too peppery, which is normal in spite of the parsley. Reber still found them delicious, she would make some at her niece's, she was very pleased with this simple, economical recipe which she had improvised with Marie, in other words with the benefit of her wisdom. Apostolos preferred the usual ratatouille but to avoid a shouting match she added that this made a change that's what we need, a little change from time to time, we appreciate it more when we get back to normal. Incorrect. After that we appreciate our everyday fare more. After that we appreciate... That wasn't quite her turn of phrase but that was what it meant. A whole programme, that phrase. The parsley of my days. What could that be. Find the right seasoning every time, depending on the day. Won't I end up always having the same one. Remember parsley. Fonfon asked for some water. Reber said no. She'd assumed exclusive rights to the carafe, she'd moved it closer to her with that intention. The intention to refuse. Gaston said no doubt about it they are too peppery, pass me the carafe please. He helped himself first, to put her off the scent, then he half-filled Fonfon's glass and Fonfon swallowed it in one gulp. Marie shouted from the kitchen fried eggs for everyone, Apostolos wanted hers boiled, three minutes. Reber pointed out to her that Marie would cook it either too much or not enough and that she had been running around all afternoon, might as well simplify her task. I shouted to Marie yes for everyone. Fonfon too would have preferred his boiled, I told him tomorrow. He wanted some more water. I didn't dare. He was wriggling on his chair, I told him go on then and come back right away. Reber's mug. He came back through the kitchen with Marie, he'd drunk from the faucet, his shirt was soaked. He didn't want to come in. Marie told him get a move on, I'm going to burn my fingers. She put the dish down on the table saying I won't change the plates, that'll season the eggs, she hadn't added any seasoning. We ate the eggs but they weren't fresh. Reber took advantage of this to say to Apostolos you see it was a good thing we didn't have them boiled. Fonfon didn't want his, he wasn't hungry, I told him to take a peach from the dumbwaiter and go into the garden. Reber started off again about principles. Apostolos had some egg yolk on her chin which stayed there the whole evening. Madame Erard is the only one kind enough to give her a little hint in such cases. Unless the others don't notice. Personally I don't dare. Or does it amuse me a little. Then cheese, Marie had bought some more but not any blue. Then peaches, then coffee in the craproom.

Reber pours the coffee. Two lumps of sugar for Apostolos, two for me, one for Gaston. I don't take sugar. She went back to her knitting. Gaston looking through the washing machine brochure, which is permanently installed on the little Moroccan table. Apostolos asked me whether I'd like a game of bezique. Courage. She married the king of hearts to the queen of diamonds. She told me I played better than Madame Cointet, it's odd, when she's so used to card games. Marie came back to collect the cups. She must have been bored in her kitchen, she was trying to think of something to say. She couldn't find anything and I couldn't be bothered to find something for her. She went out again. Bezique. No, you've got it wrong again, it's the queen of spades and the jack of hearts, not the opposite, look, this is the opposite. She said it's funny, I get it wrong every time. After that we talked about when they were going on holiday. Reber was leaving at the beginning of September, Apostolos wasn't going away. She wouldn't wear her beautiful dress.

This time it's finished.

The little future has gone west.

Say what I did after they went up to bed. Gaston was in his armchair, lost in thought. I said why don't you go and stay with your mother, that would take your mind off things. He told me she isn't very well, my sister is going to look after her. He went to sort his bills.

NOTES

page 52

Therese Neumann (b. 1898) Bavarian visionary, who received the stigmata during Lent 1926.

page 54

Houdon (1741-1828), Carpeaux (1827-1875) French sculptors, whose work was much appreciated and reproduced during the nineteenth century.

Speech given by Robert Pinget
on October 1, 1982
at
A Retrospective Colloquium
on the Nouveau Roman
at New York University—The Center for
French Civilization and Culture

translated by Barbara Wright

I have not a great deal to add to the remarks I made at the Cerisy conference on the New Novel a few years ago, for I have always worked along the same lines. (These remarks, incidentally, were reprinted as a postface to the translation of one of my novels published here by Red Dust, *The Libera me Domine*.) What I can do, though, is go into greater detail about the way I treat the material of my novels, and try to explain how I write them.

In fact, since what is still, I believe, called "The New Criticism" —an offshoot of the science of Linguistics, with which it is even sometimes confused—since the New Criticism has seized on our work, it seems that we authors have no option but to take a stand on this discipline, whether it be to reject or to accept it. It has to some extent impugned the author, even going so far as to throw doubt on the importance of his role. These critics no longer talk of creation, they talk of production, which they see as something like the result of all the forces arising out of intertextuality as a generalized phenomenon.

The positive aspect of this way of envisaging literature is the importance the new critics attach to the study of the text as such: that is to say, as the field of interaction of signifiers.

But the risk it runs, if I understand it aright, is that, if taken to extremes, any text by any writer would qualify as food for thought, as if all texts issued, and could only issue, from the same universal mechanism, and as if the only thing that mattered was to understand its functioning, without bothering any longer to ask ourselves either why, or with what aim, it functions. If that were the case, it would be the end of any scale of values.

Unless this criticism were to decide to confine its attentions to the texts of a few élite writers whose sole preoccupation was precisely to please it, and who refused themselves the flights of fancy arising, for example, from spontaneity—the *bête noire* of this criticism. In that case, however, it would have become too selective, and no longer have the audience which, after the improvement of its methods and the broadening of its views, it deserves to reach.

It would be logical, as things stand at the moment, for the authors who have whole-heartedly subscribed to the spirit of this discipline, to stop signing their texts, since they admit that they do not have exclusive rights to them. Yet they continue to sign them. This, then, is a phenomenon we should keep in mind.

So far as I personally am concerned, I have taken a great interest in the work of this new school because it has helped me to a better understanding of the movement of my texts, and to become aware of an element of their significance that is not negligible. But it is ideally impossible for me to exclude from my writings the totally subjective side they contain, and the light they throw on my most secret intentions. My work does not solely consist in discovering the functioning of the text on the page, but also in trying to discover where my choice of words comes from, and the relationship to my aspirations that they may signify.

What I call the *tone of voice* is nothing other than the deliberate choice of a certain vocabulary, and it is the sum total of this vocabulary that is alone responsible for breathing life into the text. This choice differs in each of my books, and is the result of a simple preoccupation with change and renewal. In the same way, it implies a different syntax from one book to the next.

This means that I only partially subscribe to the idea that a text is merely a production; in other words, a game deliberately played with the purely material inter-relationship of signs. Even though, of course, my writings no longer contain any representation in the classical sense, they do still contain something eminently subjective, which is the search for a personal expression. It is just possible that my books may simply be exercises in the control of my creative faculty, of my sensations, of my memory. Exercises in the mastery of the tone, which may take various forms.

People today still talk a great deal about Mallarmé, and about his dream of the ideal Book—an object independent of any other concept than that of pure beauty. But they forget that, apropos of *Hérodiade*, he wrote in a letter: This poem... "into which I put the whole of myself without realizing it... and to which I finally found the key."

This is to say that he himself, whose all-embracing consciousness has been so much praised, accepts not only the participation of the unconscious in writing, but also the fact that a poetic text reflects the temperament of the author, and that it can therefore be a way for him to know himself.

Mallarmé also wrote, elsewhere: "On paper, the artist creates himself," and not: "the artist creates." Here he implicitly recognizes the expessive role of the text, and he never, to my knowledge, went so far as to deny the author as a unique individual or, consequently, the significance of writing in so far as it is concerned with other than purely functional phenomena.

On this same subject, it would be difficult to be more lucid than Baudelaire, who wrote in the preface to one of his translations of Edgar Allan Poe, *Nouvelles histoires extraordinaires*: "But above all, I want to say that, having allotted the proper share to the natural poet, to *innateness*, Poe also allotted a share to science, to work, and to analysis—which will seem exorbitant to those who are arrogant but not erudite."

And again, comparing Poe to those poets who believed solely in disorder and whose aim was to write poems with their eyes closed: "... likewise, Edgar Allan Poe—one of the most inspired men I have ever known—made an effort to hide his *spontaneity*, to simulate sang-froid and deliberation."

Innateness, spontaneity, inspiration, which I assimilate with the unconscious, with its most immediate manifestations which will then be controlled: on reflection, this is self-evident.

I have great respect for the present-day critical methods, and I even owe a debt of gratitude to those who employ them, since they have been good enough to turn their attention to my work, but I don't think that, given the still very new state of the science from which they are derived, these methods are the only ones capable of making an exhaustive assessment of the value of a text.

It is not solely in the light of pure deductive reasoning that my books should be approached, for in so far as it is possible I allow them to be activated by the irrational, particularly in their sequences. Why? A question of idiosyncrasy, of temperament. In my eyes, the share allotted to the irrational is one of the ways that may help me to arrive at a personal "truth," which is only to a very limited extent present in my awareness of it. This is a kind of open provocation to the unconscious. This "truth," while it is no more important than that of anyone else, is nevertheless more valuable to me, if only because it helps me to a better-informed approach to the truths of other people. We are all, indeed, more or less dependent on the collective unconscious, whose nature we can only glimpse by examining as best we can those manifestations of it which we perceive in ourselves.

I don't know whether this proposition is orthodox: I mean, that the fact of intentionally having recourse to the irrational causes some revelation of the unconscious to emerge, but it seems to me that the magic of primitive peoples did not work otherwise, and that the study of its practices has taught us many things; side by side, of course, with the interpretation of dreams, which doesn't date from today, though the irrational discourse of dreams is not released intentionally.

All this does not mean to say that the "psychological" significance of my work is more important to me than its aesthetic significance; I am merely trying to avert the error people may fall into if they consider that once my book has been closed, nothing should remain but the pleasure —or the boredom—of having read it. Something more, something indefinable, fortunately, is intended to be its distinguishing characteristic. To my mind, this characteristic can only be perceived by a kind of criticism that does not belong to any school but which dips more or less at random into my work.

In short, it is by a very personal method, and in the actual process of writing, that I criticize my manner of understanding literature, and I can only do this in terms that are not in common use. This criticism is an integral part of my work. And it is the reason why I have never felt a need to construct a theory independently of my writings.

If it is *de rigueur*, in this assembly, to speak of technique, I will very briefly say that the structure of my novels is often built on recurrences. These recurrences, or repetitions, are of four kinds.

1) Complete recurrence, *ab initio*, or repetition of the first part of

the book in the second. Bipartite structure, then. Typical examples: *No Answer, Fable, The Apocrypha.* What is important here is the repetition of all the themes, but with perceptible or imperceptible modifications, distortions, variations, transfigurations, which finally destroy, or at least shake, the certainties that the reader may have fastened on in the first part. Hence the impression that the book is being composed, and decomposed, under his very eyes. The formula I have employed to define this procedure and which applies to all my books is: *Nothing is ever said, since it can be said otherwise*

2) Partial and progressive recurrence, all the way through the book. After a certain number of pages, let's say, recapitulation of themes with variations, and so on with different themes. Typical examples: *Someone, The Libera me Domine, Passacaglia.* "Unipartite" structure, then.

3) Complete but reversed recurrence, starting from the middle of the book, of the first part in the second, which thus repeats it by going back to the beginning. Bipartite structure, but disguised as "unipartite," as the book is all of a piece. This is what I have called anamnesis. Unique example: *That Voice.* Variations and hypotheses proliferate as in 1) and 2). It is only the stimulus that differs. I would therefore stress the fact that in order to write, I need a positive stimulus to trigger the creative process.

A fourth kind of recurrence is the pure and simple repetition of certain key-phrases or *leitmotifs* throughout the book, which thus increase its resemblance to a musical composition. These repetitions, or refrains, are additional to the three other kinds of recurrences and are to be found in almost all my novels. I like to use them, because they are more effective than all the others in creating an impression of surface unity. The difficulties in reading caused by the variations on the themes are thus, in my eyes, or rather, in my ears, smoothed out. And the reason why it is these *leitmotifs* that I am the most attached to is, it seems to me, because they persuade me that in spite of my liking for combinatorial games, the most important thing to me is to convince myself, and to make the reader convince himself, that once a work of art has assimilated all possible complexities of expression, its aim must be to say only one simple thing which, I think, is called poetry.

This part of my technique, which I can describe only very succinctly here, is relatively easy to apply and to analyze. Its effect on the writing itself, on what the reader reads, is another matter. He is hindered by an abundance of assertions and negations, of alterations, second thoughts, parallels, distortions; in short, by an apparent absence of logic.

But the logic, or reasoning, of art, is not that of logic. Art is always founded in nature, but reconstitutes it in a different way, makes it into something greater, more beautiful, more true, less immediately apprehensible. Of course, the criterion of this beauty and this truth changes from century to century and from artist to artist. This is a truism.

My own way of exalting nature has been to make people discover, or to try to make them discover, its infinite variety. What I have called its *potentialities*, which are all included in a given reality. The imagination is in fact a constituent part of our being, and is just as necessary as dreams and observation.

Every time I tackle a new book, my temperament incites me not to give it exactly the same form as its predecessor, in other words, the same language or the same tone, which are indissolubly linked to its form. The result of my way of working is that each book is different right from the outset. But very fortunately, whatever I do, my readers say that no matter which of my books they tackle, they recognize the same voice in it. I say very fortunately because, all things considered, the essential for me, in these experiments, is to explore and throw light on what my innermost depths conceal, and this I can only achieve by means of successive trial and error.

My attachment to the technique of the intermingling of themes and their variations is due to the admiration I have always felt for so-called baroque music. When I was very young I was already captivated by it, and for years I tried to exalt its spirit in rather maladroit poems. It was only later that I pursued the idea of taking inspiration from it in the novel. This may seem inconsistent, after what I have just said about the deliberate irrationality of my writings, for the type of music in question goes to great pains to set an example of the most rigorous geometry. In this connection we should remember the accusations made in the nineteenth century against baroque music, and against its grandiose and disconcerting discoveries. Invention, experimentation, and the unexpected, are triumphant in this music thanks to an exceptional mastery of means. Is there any need to mention the mirror-image technique employed by the greatest representative of this school? The irrational, controlled and measured in masterly fashion, is the very well-spring of his creative power.

It is piquant to remember that in the last century this form of art was considered to be "chaotic, cultural muck!"

But to pursue this analysis of the relation of my work to that of composers who include one of the most formidable past-masters of all time, would be to condemn it to the most inevitable shipwreck.

I would be better advised to say, merely, that for thirty years I have devoted myself to a kind of experimental writing that is intimately linked to oral expression. My exercises in vocabulary, syntax, rhythm, punctuation, have always been aimed at trying to match this writing to the voice that inspires it. My ear catches something that my pen endeavours to transcribe. My books are to be listened to, rather than to be read.

As for the subjects treated in my novels, they are taken from the most banal, apparently derisory, everyday events, *in which there is nothing that can make a novel*, but which I have chosen for my material. This is to say, given the importance I attach to every well-thought-out formulation, that I play on this appearance to the point of exhausting it, in order to make anyone who listens to me admit that, beneath or beyond appearances, a drama is being played out. Now, if this drama is being played out, the game must be to give the listener a premonition of it—one must play fair—or "play the game." A lucid activity, in other words gratuitous, hence necessary. Every work of art is a more or less dangerous game, which may well be mortal. Let us not forget that drama is an essential act of nature which is played out in the innermost depths of the being, and hence moved by passion, moved by pathos. Once again, these are all truisms.

Their horror of passing time, of the everyday, has the paradoxical effect of making my narrators cling to these everyday events in order to reduce them to nothingness. Hence their constant, liberating repetitions, and their open access to the world of the imagination. The systematic confusion of grammatical tenses and of situations is symptomatic of this need to annihilate the obstacle. This quest to discover something else through the medium of the imagination only retains its character to the extent to which the narrators decide to forget what they are looking for, fascinated as they are by the discovery itself, and fearing more than anything else that they might glimpse the beginning of the end of their spiritual adventure. In other words, they have no option but to despise death, which would be the end of the Word; this they do by flushing it out everywhere, and demystifying it with humour. A task which could not be more vain, as they well know, but they accept it, once again because of their liking for the game. They are therefore perfectly cognizant of their extravagance but it is the rule of this procedure, which might seem absurd to anyone who had no sense of liberty.

Let me repeat that my work belongs to the domain of art, and that I use every artifice of language in it, amongst which contradiction is by no means the least. Thus, to go no farther than this element of contradiction, which is the most obvious and simplistic form of variation, a casual reader may well find that contradiction is the only thing he remembers after his quick reading of my books, but this would be to amputate them of three quarters of their content, not to say the whole.

If I do not quote any of my other books here, it is because their composition is simpler and more apparent. They are no less typical, each in its own way—I am thinking in particular of *The Inquisitory*—of my constant and primordial concern with tonality, with the exigencies of my ear, and of my declared intention, from my very first book, to extend the limits of the written word by replenishing it with the spoken word. I felt an urgent need to adopt this language deliberately, with its particularities of syntax, its inventions, and its rich vocabulary.

My first novels all reflect this fascination with these potentialities, which then manifested themselves more freely. All the suggestions, refutations, prolongations and metamorphoses of fragments of speech are deliberately expressed in them. A more rigorous disposition or composition of these fragments imposed itself later, but the material has remained the same.

But if I were to try to make this exposé more systematic, I would run the risk of falsifying or restricting the meaning of my writings, and that would be to betray them.

After thirty years of publication with *Les Éditions de Minuit*, I am still affiliated to the New Novel and I still stand by its efforts and discoveries, which are of great diversity, and undeniable present-day significance. For my part, by the choice of a method of which I have given you only the barest outline, I have attempted an approach to the dark face of language, in order to make it easier for unconscious values to break through and thus enlarge the field of my conscious activity. This has involved reconciling innateness with calculation, and often putting the accent on paradox which, as Jung said, is one of our supreme spiritual values.

To end on a more general note, I should like to read you a short paper I wrote in 1977 for the Mainz Academy, of which I am proud to be a corresponding member. This institution was conducting a little inquiry into what is entitled "Literary Baggage" (Literatur als Gepäck).

Here is my reply:

To say baggage is to say voyage... The journey we undertake without a travel agency, and without having chosen it. The journey that lasts a lifetime. "Did you have a good journey?" It is the privilege of those whose baggage has been well packed to be able to answer yes. What will they have put into it? The thing that weighs the least, and whose name is: wisdom. It is vigilant, and it devours the kind of time that is always doing its utmost to prevent us from continuing our crossing: chronological time. Could there be another kind, then? Yes, that of childhood, of legend, the time of myths, of origins. *That* time has no weight, for it is a product of the Word. We have access to it when we listen to what was said in the beginning, the memory of which we have all retained in our innermost depths. *In illo tempore*, in that primordial time, which remains and does not pass, we were told truths which were soon written down. So the Word was consecrated by the Letter, and was called Legend—*that which is to be read*. All literature, whether sacred or profane, has its source in this ancient, mysterious process.

The sole "baggage" that helps us to conquer chronological time and to participate in the other, absolute time, is a bouquet of texts, an anthology which we are able to refer to at every moment of our existence. These texts may be of a different nature, but they nevertheless have the same far-distant origin. The *homo religiosus*, linked to the essential—if we admit his presence in every one of us—rebels against the lacerations produced by the succession of days, and seeks refuge in the time which knows neither succession nor laceration, that of the Word.

Light baggage, buzzing with words, which, ever since the world has been the world—and there are many legends that vouch for it—has ensured our passage, without let or hindrance, over on to the other bank.

The "Trials" of Translating Pinget

by Barbara Wright
Written for the Review of Contemporary Fiction, June 1983.

When, out of the blue, I received a letter from John O'Brien suggesting that I might like to write something about "the trials of translating Pinget," I answered by return that I would love to — provided that I could substitute the word "pleasures" for "trials."

For it is a truth that *should* be universally acknowledged, that whatever the difficulties and problems intrinsic to a text, it is still infinitely "easier" to translate a good writer than an indifferent one. (Another far from universally-acknowledged truth is that no text of whatever order is ever easy to translate.) And Robert Pinget is one of those rare good writers whose every word and phrase is there for its own particular purpose; no other could be substituted for it. It is, of course, an enormous challenge to try to match such an impeccable use of language, but it is partly this challenge that makes the work of translation so enjoyable.

Are there any specific problems in translating Pinget that do not apply to the work of most of the other admirable French writers I have translated? There are some, yes, but in general the difficulties are much the same.

In works which, for want of a better term, I describe to myself as "poetic prose," the translator comes up against many of the same problems that confront the translator of poetry. He has to try to reproduce the rhythm, the assonance, the pace, the harmonics, the allusions, of the original. Not to mention its semantics. (What's more, he often gets the odd casual pun thrown in for good measure.) I have come to take it as axiomatic that some poetry really, *really* is untranslatable, because of the very richness of its component elements. Which often, of course, also include rhyme. If all these elements are of more or less equal importance, then sometimes, something has to go—and this is when a poem becomes untranslatable.

(*Parenthesis*: Raymond Queneau once wrote to me that he had always known that nothing was untranslatable—but I think he must have had only prose in mind. Even though he, like Pinget, always strongly maintained that he saw no essential difference between poetry and prose. However that may be, Queneau later amused himself by writing a poem containing a mere four lines. The first three were taken up with a pun on the two meanings of "fils de la Vierge": 1) gossamer, and 2) son of the Virgin. The fourth, devastating line, cruelly consisted of: "allez me traduire ça en anglais"!

Underlying, and fundamental to all the elements combined in poetic writing is its tone of voice. In a note to his *Le Libera*, Pinget wrote: "It seems to me that the interest of my work up to the present has been the quest for a *tone of voice*... The tone varies from each of my books to the next. There will never be an end to my researches in this field..." This came as a revelation to me: I suddenly saw that that was the very essence of any translation worthy of the name—the attempt to reproduce the author's tone of voice. It was another, far more graphic, way of envisaging what I had always known was the aim of the translator. He merely (merely!) has to produce what the author would have written had he happened to be writing in the language of the translation.

Your first task, then, is to try to think yourself into the author's tone of voice—or rather, to *feel* yourself into it, because this can only be a spontaneous work of the imagination which, furthermore, can probably only be achieved when you love and admire the work of "your" author.

One poetic element that is perhaps unique to Pinget is the hypnotic mystery implicit in his frequent repetitions of the same word or phrase. This calls for especial vigilance on the part of his translator; a moment's inattention and he has woefully betrayed his author. By trial and error I have found a way to guard against such betrayals. In addition to the separate exercise book that I always keep for every translation, in which I note any particular problems or nuances on which it is advisable to consult French friends, or, *in extremis*, the author—though one is reluctant to bother him unnecessarily—I now keep an alphabetical, cross-referenced index for each Pinget book. "Le calme. Le gris." (*Passacaille*), 10 repetitions. "Le fruit de vos entrailles" (*Fable*), 5 repetitions." *Manque un raccord*" (Cette Voix), 17 repetitions. This may sound a horribly cold-blooded, pedestrian, pedantic way to approach a poetic translation, but I assure you that without such a basic analysis one cannot possibly achieve the subtle aims that I have mentioned. Let alone get anywhere near the reproduction of what is always present between the lines in Pinget—the inexpressible.

I maintain that the translator is the person best placed to appreciate the quality of any writer. Just think, for instance, of all that analysis, pedestrian or otherwise, which he has to undertake before he even begins his translation. That is why I am so confident of my opinion of Pinget's writing. And also why I am equally confident when I say that the more times you read his books, the more layers of meaning, feeling and truth you find in them.

In the French anthology "How Writers Work," Pinget wrote that "After the first draft, three or four versions are necessary." These subsequent versions are, *a fortiori*, even more necessary for a Pinget translation. But can this be called a "trial"? Far from it! It sometimes even happens that when you arrive at your *very* final version, your unconscious, after months of dithering, will have done its work, and will present you with something that you are almost convinced is the best that can be found.

What's the opposite of a trial? A blessing? Maybe. Well, one of the blessings of translating Pinget is the help he is always willing to provide, in infinitely generous measure. You make a stupid mistake? It is with the utmost, kindly discretion that he merely hints at it. You do something just right? He calls it "joli," or even "superbe." And he always allows you to feel that you are working in cooperation with him for the benefit of the work, for the sake of the thing-in-itself.

BARBARA WRIGHT